MW00379532

BEHIND BARS

Bar Coding Principles and Applications

BEHIND BARS

Bar Coding Principles and Applications

PETER L. GRIECO, JR.

MICHAEL W. GOZZO

C. J. (CHIP) LONG

PT PUBLICATIONS, INC.
4360 NORTH LAKE BLVD.
PALM BEACH GARDENS, FL 33410
(407) 624-0455

Library of Congress Cataloging in Publication Data

Long, C. J.
Behind bars: bar coding principles and applications / C. J. Long, with Peter L. Grieco, Jr. and Michael W. Gozzo.
Bibliography;
Includes index.
1. Product coding. I. Grieco, Peter L., 1942- . II. Gozzo, Michael W., 1939- . III. Title.
HF5416.L66 1989
006.4'2—dc19

89-3167
CIP

ISBN 0-945456-03-4

Printed in the United States of America

TABLE OF CONTENTS

PREFACE

Every day, it seems, the field of bar coding adds another area to its already long list of beneficial functions.

Right now, firms across the country and throughout the world are discovering for themselves why industries such as hospitals, groceries and retail stores have applied bar coding technology for years with significant benefits. Given this fact, the question is why haven't American companies fully participated in a technology that not only reduces costs dramatically, but offers a unique opportunity to control the whole manufacturing process?

This book answers that question. It shows you how to take advantage of current ideas and opportunities which will assist you in developing, implementing and maintaining the optimal bar coding solution for your company. That means a system which is easy to use, fast and, above all, accurate.

Getting started is ***not*** as difficult as the current literature with its forbidding jargon might lead you to believe. ***Behind Bars*** was written for people who want to implement a far more profitable and productive means of controlling and tracking information and material that has verifiable results.

What are some of these results?

- Maximized productivity while planning order picking.
- Visibility and inspection from dock to stock.
- Collection of accurate shop floor data.
- Collection of quality control data.
- Improved management of material control functions.
- Improved reporting of production processes.
- Interfaces with cost and accounting systems.
- Provisions for sophisticated inventory management.

As you can readily see, bar coding is much more than "beeps" at a supermarket checkout counter. In fact, its advantages over other means of entering data are considerable.

ADVANTAGE #1: SPEED

A bar code label of twelve characters can be wanded in approximately the time it takes a keyboard operator to make two keystrokes.

ADVANTAGE #2: ACCURACY

For every 1,000 characters typed by a keyboard operator, there are an average of ten keying errors. For an Optical Character Reader (OCR), there is one error in every 10,000 reads. With wands, bar coding systems approach one error in every 3,000,000 characters and with laser technology, they approach one error in 70 million entries.

ADVANTAGE #3: DATA INTEGRITY

Probable number of substitution errors for every 3,400,000 characters entered:

Keyboard Entry	10,000
OCR Scanning	300
Bar Coding (Code 39)	1

ADVANTAGE #4: EASE OF IMPLEMENTATION

Operators of bar code scanners can learn to use the equipment effectively in less than 15 minutes. System costs are lower than other means of data entry because of the existence of interfacing hardware and software.

ADVANTAGE #5: COST EFFECTIVENESS

Bar coding has a demonstrated payback period of six to eighteen months.

In short, bar coding has the proven highest level of reliability. Should you entrust your company's information to anything less?

Often, we are asked: Where can I use bar coding? Our reply is: If it moves, if it is counted or if it needs to be accounted for, then bar coding has an application. As for industries in which bar coding is used, a partial list would include the following as major participants:

- Hospitals.
- Libraries.
- Manufacturing.
- Military.
- Retail.
- Grocery.
- Transportation.
- Distribution.

And within these industries, bar coding performs the following functions (among many others):

- Counting.
- Data collection.
- Information call-up.
- Signalling to conveyor director gates.
- Send-ahead orders and instructions.
- Selection and control of machine instructions.
- Instruction and control of production line robots.

This is only a glimpse at what bar coding can offer. Its application is only limited by the creativity of people. And we still believe that America's creativity will never run dry.

C.J. (Chip) Long
June 1989

ACKNOWLEDGEMENTS

We wish to thank all the people (in the thousands) who are clients or have attended our Bar Coding programs throughout the world for their active support and examples of what we call the Total Business Concept. Equally important have been the interactions with some of our consulting staff: Mel Pilachowski, Phil Stang, Mike Stanko, Wayne Douchkoff and Paul Hine. We thank them for their examples, anecdotes and suggestions in this book.

In particular, we would like to thank Jerry W. Claunch for his long and continuous support as Senior Vice President of Professionals for Technology Associates, Inc. We wish him success on the publication of his book with Phil Stang on Set-Up Reduction which will be available in early 1990.

Another pillar of support has been provided by our capable office staff of Rita Grieco, Leslie Echelson, Dawn Souby and Kevin Grieco. Still more support came from Debi Zitzler, Sandy Claunch and Gay Long, all of whom understood the time spent developing this book. In addition, we thank Dick Maccabe for his illustrations which contribute much to the text. Special thanks also go to the companies which supplied us with art work which explains key concepts.

As always, we would like to express our continued appreciation to a major member of the team, Steven Marks, for his editorial assistance in preparing yet another book in a series which covers today's most urgent manufacturing problems and their solutions.

We hope that your reading will be as pleasurable as our efforts.

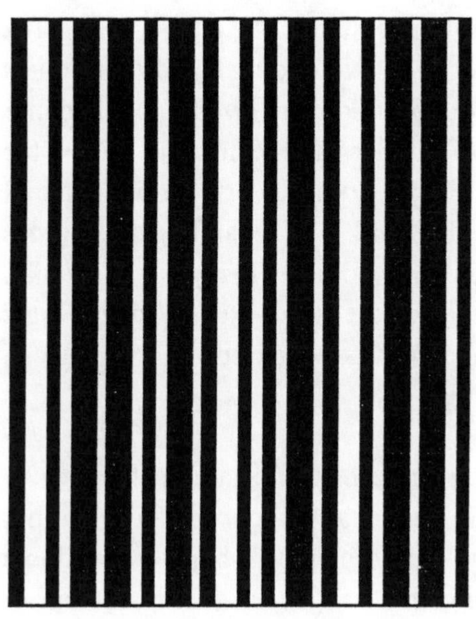

CHAPTER ONE: Introduction to Bar Coding

For the moment, let's forget about how bar coding is sweeping the nation and concentrate on something more basic. Chances are that you have picked up this book to read because you want to get beyond the equipment and systems required for bar coding. You want to know ***how*** bar coding can work for you.

It is ironic that an industry founded by problem-solvers pays so little attention to this demand. The bar coding industry was developed by people who were solving problems for companies. Therefore it is inherently an applications industry. This book tries not to forget that legacy and become overwhelmed by the latest and greatest story. Furthermore, this book is not a technological treatise with jargon you won't understand. The industry has left a void in the area of explaining what bar coding can do for you. It is a simple, but often forgotten, axiom that you can't become committed to what you don't understand. Smart investors, for example, never put their money into an enterprise or financial offering which they don't understand. Understanding only comes from education. Commitment only comes when you understand. And success only comes when you are committed. With this logic in mind, we have addressed in this book the issue of how you can successfully apply bar coding.

Commitment means making the effort and taking the time to educate all potential users in a company about the basics of bar coding. If a company fails to do its homework when it comes down to education, then keep in mind that no state-of-the-art software or hardware will cover up ignorance.

The implementation of bar coding must be non-technical in order to be successful. When Material Requirements Planning (MRP) and Manufacturing Resource Planning (MRP II) were first introduced, we made the mistake of emphasizing the technological side. It took many years to overcome this self-imposed hurdle. We can't expect people to embrace bar coding if we only feed them technological details without first showing them the basics and how they can be applied.

This book grew out of a demand for "how-to's". Our staff has been conducting bar coding seminars in Europe, Japan, Canada and this country for the last five years. At each seminar, we ask attendees to introduce themselves and tell why they have attended. The responses are virtually all the same in spite of industry differences: people want to know how to solve their problems. Here are some of the typical responses that we have heard time and time again:

COMPANY	REASON FOR ATTENDING
Microwave cables, antennas and asssemblies for military purposes	Want to learn applications and see what bar coding can do for us.
Biotechnology firm—blood	Want to use bar coding for documentation and to track paperwork flow.
Wholesale seafood supplier	Educate ourselves about bar coding so we can use it to track quantities and foreign shipments.
Commercial and industrial sewing machine company	Applications; also getting pressure from company we deal with to use bar coding.
Phototypesetter manufacturer	Applications.
Power cutting tool manufacturer	To learn more about bar coding and what applications have the best payback.

Computer manufacturers	Practical advice: systems design, start-up costs, hidden costs.
	Track material for inventory purposes, reduce costs, tie into MRP system.
	Mostly to meet customer requirements, but also to use bar coding for quality and shop floor control.
	Like to get additional applications beyond what we already have.
	Exposure to bar coding history and applications in order to use in new, fully-automated facility.
Automotive supplier	Customers demanding bar code labels on shipped products; want to see further possible application for our company.
Golf ball manufacturer	Education; in the process of designing new plant and want to incorporate bar coding from start.
Construction trade supplier	Looking at bar coding to track products, receipts, process, finished goods and to improve accuracy.

Distributors	Lot tracking, product labeling, warehousing and inventory; want to hire consultant to provide guidance.
	How to implement bar coding; how to get better information on Work-In-Process (WIP).
Pharmaceutical company	Have a proposal for bar coding systems design; want to check proposal.
Data acquisition company	Want to expand bar coding into quality tracking.
Measuring instruments manufacturer	Put bar coding labels on products to customers; how can we use the labels internally?
Tool manufacturer	Want to track tools in crib.
Retail chain supplier	How to help suppliers implement a compatible bar coding system.

Some useful conclusions can be derived from this list. First, note the wide range of companies. Bar coding has applications in almost any company you can imagine. Second, participants overwhelmingly came for two reasons: education and applications. Third, people were looking to increase benefits, reduce costs, improve accuracy or control assets and processes. Fourth, some attendees were already beginning to see the next wave of bar coding applications in areas like Just-In-Time, Total Quality Control and automation. They saw that there is an urgent need to manage data rapidly and accurately in the focus factory.

It should also be noted that the majority of the attendees were not technical personnel or engineers. Many companies, in fact, saw the value in educating a number of people who would eventually be responsible for implementation. To give you an idea of the people who are interested in bar coding, let's review some of their titles:

President/Chief Executive Officer
Chief Financial Officer
Warehouse managers
Manufacturing engineer
Machine shop manager
Inventory manager
Distribution and Logistics manager
Industrial engineers — senior, staff, manager, supervisors
Manufacturing systems coordinator
Project manager
Manufacturing engineers — all levels
Shipping/Receiving manager
Office manager
Manager of Information Systems
Operations managers
Materials Handling managers
Project leader, Manufacturing Systems
Design engineering and tool design personnel
Purchasing managers
Material managers
Financial managers

People ***are*** interested in bar coding. From our experience in implementation, we can state that people's major interests lie in th following areas:

1. Learning how to maximize bar coding's potential.

2. Staying on the leading edge with their competition and current with their customers' demands.

3. Looking for more possible internal applications.

4. Implementing bar coding in a new facility.

5. Controlling inventory accuracy.

6. Reducing manual data entry functions.

For the most part, the literature about bar coding has touched on these interests by tabulating results. Bar coding can either increase or improve your productivity, asset management, resource allocation, real time information, labor productivity, inventory control, production control, customer service or operating costs. Bar coding can certainly do all this and much more, but people are hungry to know where bar coding can be applied. When looked at in this manner, the true benefits of bar coding are much more basic and much more applicable to all facets of a business. Tabulations tend to put blinders on us and keep us from using bar coding in inventive and novel ways. These are the basic benefits:

SPEED — rapid entering of information.
ACCURACY — virtually error-free.
RELIABILITY — built-in error checking.

Such simple benefits, however, can create amazingly beautiful and complex applications. For any of you who have seen photographs of the mathematical mappings of fractals, you can understand what we mean. Here, too, a few simple rules set up levels of complexity which are simply mind-boggling.

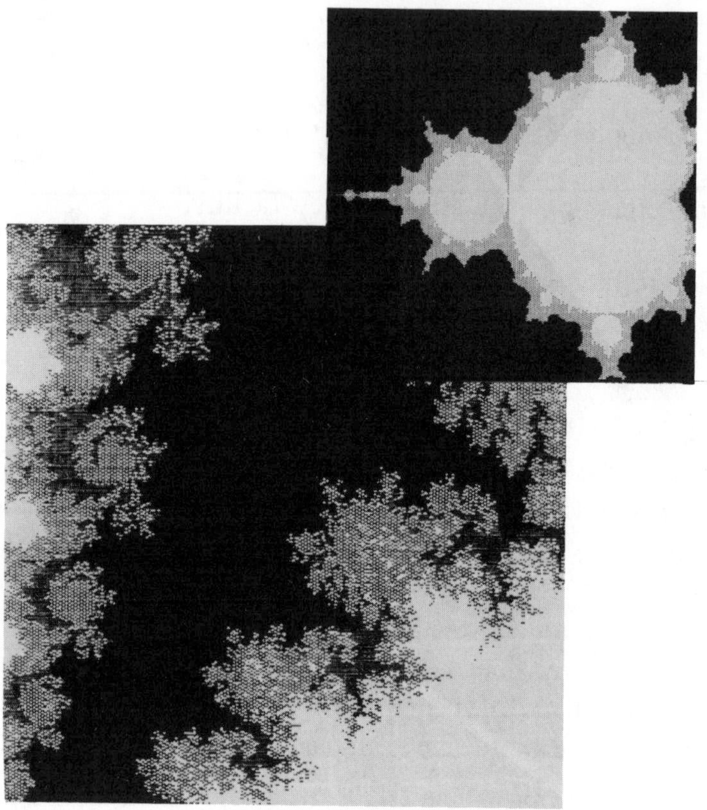

Plots of Mandelbrot Set ***by Stephen Unruh***

Talk about the simplicity, elegance and beauty of bar coding applications is not hype. The uses of bar codes still surprise us, as do the ingenious ways that companies use to maximize this industry's potential. It can't be hype alone when the industry is predicted to grow between 40% and 60% a year for the next few years. Bar coding sales for 1984 were approximately $170 million. In 1990, projections are for $1 billion. These figures should tell you something about what we must do. Some of the companies contributing to this phenomenal growth are your competitors. You must decide whether you want to automate, emigrate or evaporate.

WHAT IS A BAR CODE?

A bar code is a grouping of parallel bars (usually black) of varying widths separated by light spaces (usually white) of varying widths. It is a piano keyboard of sorts and, like the keys of a piano, each black bar and white space registers a piece of information when it is "played" in the right manner. A bar code is a "score" of information waiting to be played upon. In bar coding, the instrument is a scanning device which reads the bars and spaces and uses software to interpret their meaning.

The scanning device reads the bar code by moving a beam across the symbol. Most bar code symbols can either be scanned left to right or right to left. Whatever the method of scanning, the various bar code symbologies, or "languages," are self-checking. They register a "read" only if the entire code is scanned and only if the bar code has not been damaged by some physical means.

Bar codes also have the advantage of being developed for use by people with little or no technical knowledge. Speed, accuracy and reliability are possible without putting undue strains on the user.

A Bar Code Musician

All that is left, besides a symbology (bar code "language") and a scanner, is the presence of a printing device to print out the labels which are to be used. As you can see, bar codes are not terribly difficult to comprehend. What is difficult to grasp is the astonishing number of applications. We all know about the application of bar coding in grocery stores. According to a recent article which appeared in the *Hartford Courant* (Hartford, Connecticut: "Retailers scan joys of selling via bar codes" by Pamela Klein), bar codes are now moving into the retail industry. Everything from clothing to cosmetics to appliances is sporting little black and white labels. As the article points out, this "momentum [is] fueled by retailers' desires to improve customer service and know what's hot and what's not."

At companies like the Manchester, New Hampshire plant of Prime Computer, which manufactures CAD/CAM workstations, it's hard to find out where bar coding is not used. Every part and every piece of paper are tracked throughout the building from the receiving to the shipping dock.

Much of the confusion about bar coding applications, however, can be cleared up if we remember that:

THE PRIMARY PURPOSE OF BAR CODING IS IDENTIFICATION.

That's it, but that is everything when it comes to applying bar coding to your company, whether you use bar codes to identify products in a warehouse or to mark locations around a plant for security guards to scan as they make their rounds. In an article in *PC Week/Management* (12/19/88), such a system is described and it is noted that one "hot spot" to label is the office coffee machine. Empty pots which are left on after everybody leaves are a fire hazard. Part of a security guard's round may be to scan the label at this checkpoint to see if the machine is still on.

HISTORICAL PERSPECTIVE

Bar codes have been around longer than most of us would guess. The first patent for a bar code was in 1949. Not until the 1960s and

1970s did industrial applications come on the scene. Obviously, it is to your advantage that bar coding does have a history. One of the first applications, in which rail cars were labeled, proved to be less than a success. Labels got dirty and were difficult to scan. Only later did the rail industry realize that a preventive maintenance program was needed to support the bar coding program. Now, fortunately, we don't have to wait for the bugs to be worked out. Bar coding already does work.

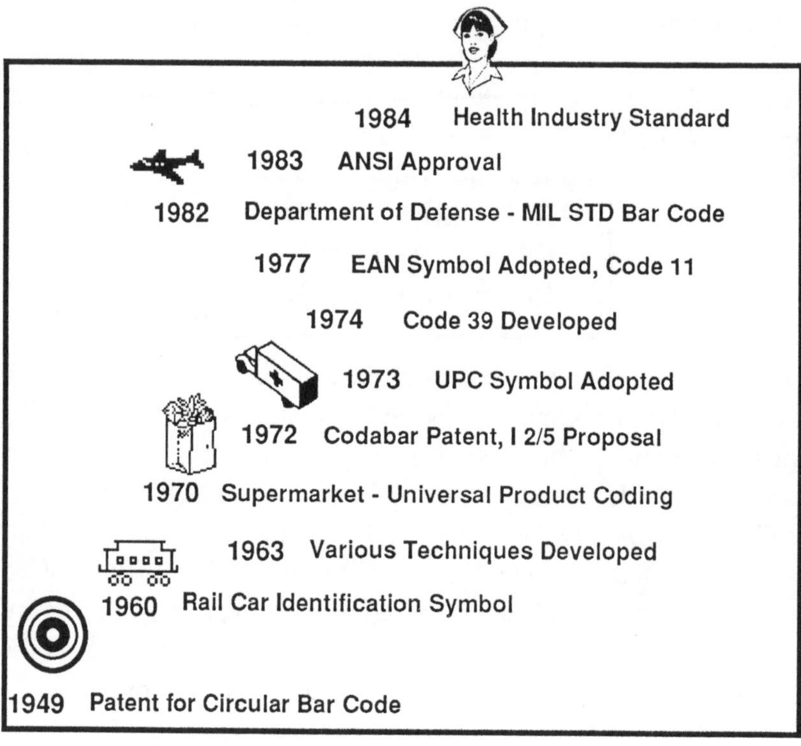

A Brief History of Bar Coding

Standardization of symbologies was another important event in bar code history. The UPC symbol was adopted in 1973. The

Department of Defense adopted a standard in 1982 and the health industry in 1984.

MAJOR BUSINESS CHALLENGES

History has shown that most bar coding problems you will encounter are the same as those already met and overcome. Companies want to get their arms around inventory, make shipping and receiving operations go faster and be more accurate, track documentation and Engineering Change Orders, etc. With ECO's, for example, it is possible to lower processing time from an average of two to three weeks all the way down to 24 hours. This is accomplished simply by knowing where the order is in the flow and by measuring queue and wait time.

Competition from other countries has forced us to look to bar coding as a way to handle problems like the ones above. When looked at in this way, then, the real reason behind implementing and using bar codes is not only to solve problems, but to uncover them as well. This has been the major focus of bar coding in the last few years and will continue to be a major thrust of bar coding in the future. For example, you may have a company with a machine shop which has drill presses in one corner and lathes in another. Like many other shops across the country, the layout bears little resemblance to the actual product flow. As you begin to implement bar coding in this typical shop, you will quickly find that the system forces you to look at how the material flows. As you decide what information to capture and where to place important measuring points, you can't avoid machine configurations. What appears to be a simple implementation ends up uncovering problems. But it is this disclosure of problems which presents a real opportunity to match your competition.

Ask Yourself the Question "Why?"

Bar coding is more like the Boston Marathon, than a 100-meter dash. You will hit the Heartbreak Hills. What you must recognize is that these are not obstacles set in your way by bar coding. The systems, computers and programs which support bar coding are

90-95% as good as they need to be. Management methods, operations and organizations, however, are only 10-20% as good as they need to be. This is the place for growth, for opportunity. This is the point where you can ask yourself: What am I trying to do? When you think you have an answer, then ask yourself the question ***"WHY?"*** five times. Remember: It's a marathon, not a sprint. Asking "why" makes you keep looking for a better answer to the problem.

Bar coding is also a race to the future. The companies which are able to link bar coding with Just-In-Time (JIT), Total Quality Control (TQC) and Computer Integrated Manufacturing (CIM) are the ones who will be meeting the major business challenges of the 1990s and beyond. The technologies and management philosophies of the future will depend on what bar coding does best:

1. Provide timely, rapid and accurate data.
2. Make data immediately available to all levels of a company.

Most business prophets envision the company of the future as being more decentralized and divided into smaller units or focused cells where all people, from the office to the floor, have responsibility and authority. Much is made over how bar coding will help managers make decisions based on up-to-the-minute information. But, the benefits of information on the shop floor are overlooked. Think how companies could control work-in-process with better information. Imagine a line worker who, while working on a job, is able to see if the next work station is on schedule or who knows whether the correct inventory is in a warehouse. This is what bar coding can do in an environment where it is often easy to forget vital information as workers and supervisors grapple with day-to-day operations and problems. Now the information is a ***scan*** away.

DATA AND INFORMATION ENTRY CHOICES

KEYBOARD DATA ENTRY

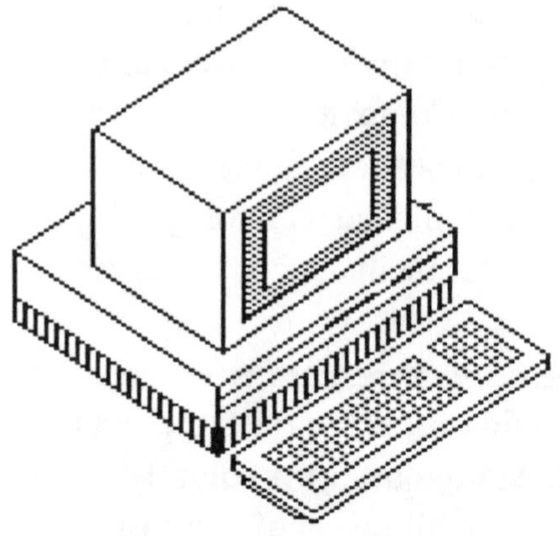

One good example of management and organization lagging behind technology can be seen in companies where the most sophisticated computer systems are fed information via a keyboard. Here, we have a company capable of on-line, real-time access to information and it runs itself as though it was still in the batch environment of the 1960s. We cannot afford to pile up data to be entered into a system in batches. We now have the capability with bar codes to enter data as it happens and demand that our computers update all related information in real time. Keyboard entry, on the other hand, is slow, dependent on human operators, inaccurate and expensive.

OPTICAL CHARACTER READERS

The great advantage of Optical Character Readers (OCR) as a means of data entry is the fact that characters can be read both by machines and people. OCRs scan printed words just like the ones you are reading now and convert them into signals which can then be understood by a computer. Despite this advantage, OCRs are inflexible. They are not resistant to spots or voids. A coffee stain, not a rare occurrence, can make a word or words unreadable. Because OCRs require the careful alignment of the printed character and the reading head, they are impractical for use with rapidly moving items as you would find on some production lines or conveyor systems. The careful orientation of character and head also makes for lower first-pass yields and numerous non-reads. In other words, it may take more than one scan to get an accurate reading. This not only slows down the process, but slows down the acceptance of the system by its users.

OCRs do have the advantage of being generally accepted in the retail industry. The labels to be read can also be printed on conventional typewriters. Bar coding's advantages, however, outweigh those of an OCR.

1. Bar coding has a lower substitution error rate. That is, readers don't misread a character and substitute the wrong letter or number when the information is fed to the computer.

2. Bar code labels can be read by non-contact devices. Obviously, this allows a degree of flexibility which is important for users who don't have a controlled environment (which is just about everybody!).

3. Bar code labels are one-dimensional, making them less sensitive to print errors and physical damage.

4. Bar codes generally require less expensive reading equipment.

5. Bar coding is better at reading long character strings. You can put much more information in an identification code of ten characters than you can in one of five characters, information like delivery date, warehouse location, shipment date, product number, etc.

MAGNETIC STRIPE TECHNOLOGY

Magnetic stripe technology has the advantages of being able to condense more information into a smaller space and alter data on the stripe. But, the data on magnetic stripes can't be read at a distance and they are more expensive than bar coding.

Bar coding has several advantages over magnetic stripes:

1. Greater versatility of scanning equipment such as reading wands, slot readers, scanners and portable readers. Scanning equipment is also cheaper than readers for magnetic stripes. A bar code wand, for example, can be bought for as little as $140.

2. Printing equipment for bar coding is also less expensive than similar equipment needed for magnetic stripes.

3. Bar code labels can be used in harsh environments where there are extreme temperatures and dirt. As noted above, we don't all have sterile laboratories in which we work.

VISION SYSTEMS

Vision systems actually digitize an object's image so that it can be understood by a computer. Thus, they not only can detect the size of an object, but whether or not a particular component is present. Vision systems are already in use in some plants doing just this sort of quality control work. High prices, however, have limited the use of vision technology. In one client's automation and robotic system, a vision system was used to locate bottles in trays. A problem developed when the company discovered that human operators were faster at picking the bottles manually. In order to correct this line imbalance, the conveyor and packaging had to be redesigned. Still, this is a very exciting field and bears watching in the future.

RADIO FREQUENCY

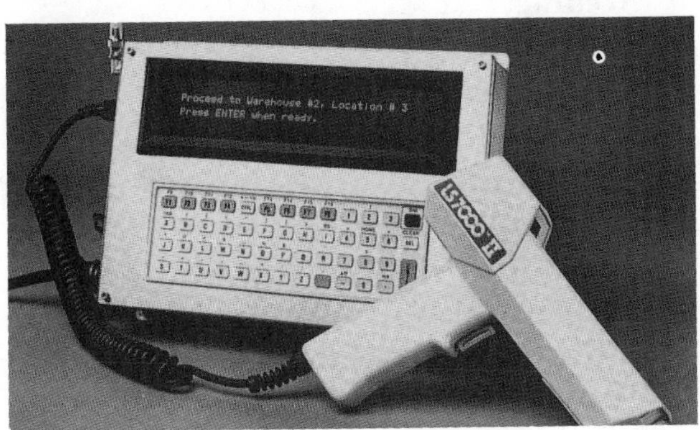

Radio Data Terminal
Photo Courtesy of Symbol MSI

Radio frequency uses a transmitting device which sends out specific radio frequencies. Special tags receive this message and respond with their own broadcast which indicates their position. The advantage here is that there is no need for physical contact or a direct line-of-sight. The disadvantage is that many shop floors have a number of machines or electrical and magnetic fields which can disrupt the transmission of radio signals. Radio frequency is used for railroad boxcar identification, warehouse operations, and animal tracking. In the last example, scientists tag anything from salmon to caribou to track their migratory wanderings.

BAR CODING ADVANTAGES

Overall, bar coding has the advantage over other data entry choices in five areas:

Speed
Accuracy
Data Integrity
Ease of Implementation
Cost Effectiveness

SPEED

The "rule of thumb" for keyboard data entry is two keystrokes per second. Using a bar code wand to scan a label of 12 characters takes two to three seconds. (Wands can scan between 400 and 600 feet per minute.) This is approximately two times the speed of a keyboard operator. It should also be noted here that read rates are directly related to speed. The industry standard for a first read rate is 85 percent. In other words, 85 percent of the time you will get a read with one sweep of the wand. The industry standard for the second read rate is 99 percent. We believe that the standard for the first read rate is too low. We believe in doing it right the first time. From a psychological viewpoint, the rate should be closer to 95 percent or else users will quickly become frustrated over the introduction of a technology that they perceive as not working right. This rate should be achieved for hand-held readers, but fixed readers (on a production line, for example) should have a first read rate of 99.9 percent simply because you can't afford to stop a line because of a misread.

Training on how to hold a wand and how to make a clean sweep with no hesitation requires about five to ten minutes of training. But, this training should be accompanied by an adequate number of hours of education which shows, along with an overview of bar coding, why good wanding techniques are critical to its success. We have assisted with an implementation at a retail store whose first read rates went from 80 percent to 99 percent in three weeks simply by emphasizing correct wanding techniques, such as speed and angle.

One last point about speed: it is affected by the size of the bar code label. Obviously, you would find it easier to scan a label the size of a bread box than the size of the head of a pin. Somewhere in between is a happy medium. Striking this balance will be covered later when we discuss label design.

ACCURACY

Because companies move literally millions of characters of information a day, there is an overwhelming need for some means to maintain accuracy. Keyboard entry does not provide that accuracy. For every 1,000 character entries, there are 10 keying errors, or an error rate of 1 percent. For data entry with the use of Optical Character Readers, accuracy improves to one error out of every 10,000 entries, or an error rate of .01 percent. Bar code accuracy greatly surpasses all other means of data entry. Using dot matrix characters, you can expect only one error in over three million entries. By using a photographic film, this can be bettered to one error in over 17 million entries. That's an error rate between approximately .00003 and .000006 percent. With laser technology, it is possible to reach the level of one error in 70 million entries, or an error rate of .0000014 percent.

DATA INTEGRITY

Looked at from the perspective of data integrity, the above information about accuracy translates into this:

PROBABLE NUMBER OF SUBSTITUTION ERRORS PER 3,400,000 CHARACTERS ENTERED

Keyboard Entry	10,000
OCR Scanning	300
Bar Coding (Code 39)	1

EASE OF IMPLEMENTATION

It doesn't take long for an operator to become proficient using bar coding equipment. With on-going training, companies which we have worked with have easily achieved 99 percent effectiveness. The problem with learning quickly and achieving high levels of proficiency is that some companies sit back and crow about their success. It can take six months to achieve the 99th percentile, but that level of excellence can disappear in less than two weeks. We have seen it happen, all because a company thought it didn't have to concern itself any more with continuous improvement and on-going education and training.

Education and Training is Job #1

At a manufacturing client in Detroit which supplies components to the automotive industry, we witnessed just how easy it was for an untrained person to master bar coding. In this company's shipping and receiving room, a woman was in charge of placing bar coding labels on products being shipped per the company's customer requirements. At this time, the company itself did not use bar coding. Over a short period of time, she learned her job so well that she began designing bar code labels to be used internally. Now, the company has its own bar coding system for in-house data collection and for tracking material and labor.

Implementing bar codes is simple also because of the ease of interfacing different components into one system. Protocol converters make it easy to transmit data collected by portable readers so that they can be "plugged" into a company's existing computer system. All of this interfacing software and hardware is relatively cheap compared to other means of data entry.

COST EFFECTIVENESS

Ultimately, it is cost effectiveness which will sell most companies and their management on bar coding. Automated scanning, of course, eliminates the need for human operators and, thus, can significantly lower costs. When people are used to scan, costs are still low in terms of training. As we have already pointed out, the learning curve for bar coding is a relatively short curve. These are apparent cost-savers, but there are less apparent ones as well. For example, what price would you put on having up-to-date and accurate information at your fingertips? Bar coding, as we have seen, can increase the productivity of both operators and managers by providing them with sufficient and necessary information to make decisions. What price do you put on the decision-making process? What cost savings would you put on morale when people can use the computer system with trust and confidence because the data is current and accurate? These are intangibles, perhaps hard to quantify, but they are nevertheless very real.

Bar coding is cost effective. It has a demonstrated payback period of six to eighteen months. We've seen it happen repeatedly in companies across the country.

WHY BAR CODING?

International Robomation/Intelligence employees recently

whipped a frisbee, with a bar code containing zip code information on its rim, past a stationary camera lens in order to prove a point to the Federal Express Corporation. The automation company was trying to prove that its camera equipment was quick enough to sort, by bar code, up to 800,000 packages flowing through Federal Express' night distribution center in Memphis, TN. The test worked and proved how far machine vision has come during the past few years.

Scanning a Frisbee

Bar code labels can be read on moving objects like frisbees at distances up to 5 feet. Hand-held readers can be up to 18 inches away from the label and still obtain accurate reads. Physical contact with the bar code label is no longer necessary which is important in less than ideal environments. Bar codes also have a high tolerance to oil, grease, moisture, dirt and other foreign materials. Bar coding is applicable in a variety of settings and is generally unaffected by magnetic or electrical fields. Perhaps in the future, we will be able to track the *Discovery* as it orbits the earth.

The dark stripe on the back of a credit card, however, is affected by magnetic fields. A fellow director and colleague at Professionals for Technology, Mike Stanko, found this out the hard way. After landing at O'Hare airport late one night, Mike found that he needed cash to get his car out of the parking lot. He found an automatic teller machine in the terminal and stuck his card in. The machine spat it out. He tried another card. The machine rejected that one, too. He tried a third with the same result. Mike then decided to try another machine in another terminal. There, he was able to get the machine to accept his card. The next day, he went to his bank to find out what went wrong. The bank told him that the first teller machine was in a high magnetic field and that it had probably wiped out the data on his cards.

All of these advantages, which are being improved continuously, add up to one thing:

BAR CODE HAS THE PROVEN HIGHEST LEVEL OF RELIABILITY.

Europe thinks so. They have the European Article Number (EAN). Japan thinks so. They have the Japanese Article Number

(JAN). Our health industry has the Health Industry Bar Coding Council (HIBCC); the auto industry has the Automotive Industry Action Group (AIAG); the government has Logistics Application of Automated Marking and Reading Symbols (LOGMARS); and the grocery industry has the Universal Product Council (UPC). What do these acronyms have to do with reliability? They indicate that a number of companies and governments found bar coding important enough to set standards. So they banded together to assure continued high levels of reliability.

A Bowl of Alphabet Soup

The number of organizations also gives some idea of bar code's many and varied applications. A list of companies, industries or organizations using bar codes would fill the majority of this book. Their applications would fill as many pages. Rather than list everything here, we have this simple answer to anybody who asks us where bar codes can be used. We tell them this:

IF IT MOVES ...
IF IT IS COUNTED ...
OR, IF IT NEEDS
TO BE ACCOUNTED FOR ...

THEN ...

BAR CODES HAVE AN APPLICATION.

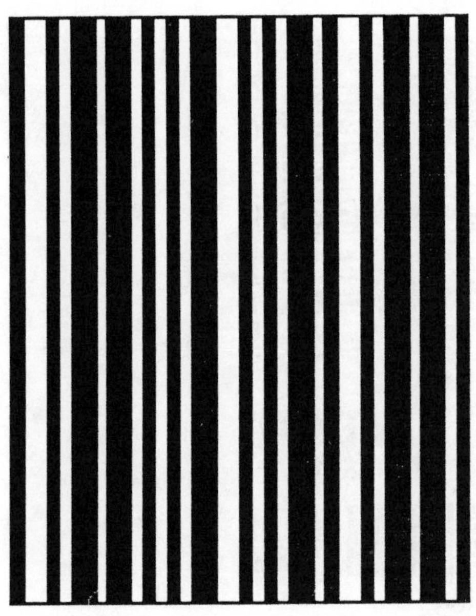

CHAPTER TWO: Symbology Definitions and Choices

If you have ever looked closely enough, you have undoubtedly noticed that not all bar codes are the same. Some have several different widths of black bars, while others only have two — one narrow and one wide. Some are longer or taller while others are more compressed and shorter. In fact, there are over 100 different bar code symbologies, some of which are shown on the next page. No single bar code can do it all; no bar code has a universal business application. That is why it is necessary for bar code shoppers to find the symbology which works best for their company or for their specific applications. Indeed, many companies use at least two different symbologies.

Assorted Bar Code Symbols

The dictionary defines symbology as the study or the interpretation of symbols. This can conjure up images of either an explorer with a pith helmet poring over scratches on a cave wall or a bespectacled English professor trying to interpret the symbols in a book by some intentionally obscure author. Bar code symbology is not like this at all. There is nothing mysterious about bar codes. They are not hieroglyphics or an ancient alphabet which takes researchers months or years to decode. The spaces and bars of a bar code are a simplified language in the manner that COBOL, BASIC and FORTRAN are simplified languages which allow programmers to speak with computers. Bar codes look "strange" because the bars and spaces are the elements of a language which can be easily understood by a computer. In essence, bar code symbologies are a sort of "in-between" language which allows humans and computers to communicate.

BAR CODE STRUCTURES

To bar coder users, symbology also refers to the set of structural characteristics which distinguishes one bar code type from another. Bar codes have five characteristics:

1 Leading quiet zone.
2 Start character.
3 One or more data characters.
4 Stop character.
5 Trailing quiet zone.

The quiet zones are necessary for the proper operation of the scanner or reader. Quiet zones are ten times the "x" dimension (width of the narrowest element) or .25 inches, whichever is greater. There is no maximum limit to the length of the quiet zone. As a general rule, too much quiet zone is better than too little. The start and stop characters also tell the scanner or reader when a bar code begins and ends. The data characters, of course, hold the information which has been encoded. All five of these characteristics are unique to each symbology. Thus, the quiet zones of Code 39 are not the same as the quiet zones of Codabar.

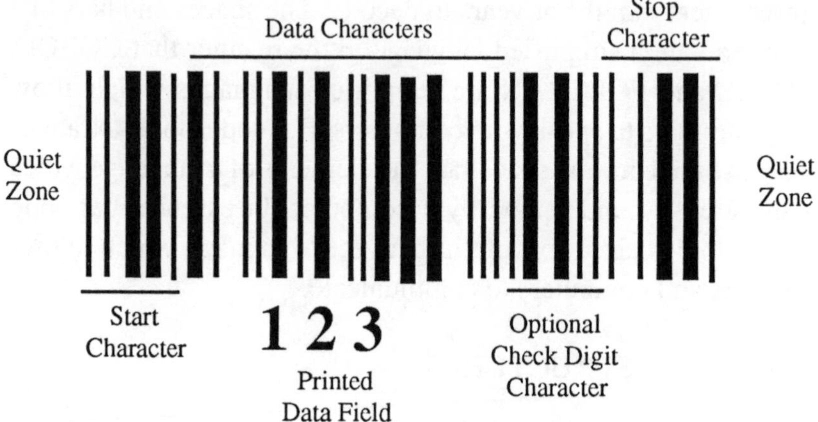

Characteristics of a Typical Bar Code

In addition to the five characteristics already noted, there are several other specifications to understand. These specifications have a direct bearing on how a particular bar code symbology is applied in a particular workplace.

The first specification is bar code ***height***. This is important from the standpoint of readability. Obviously, it is easier for an operator of a scanning device to keep the sweep of the wand within the bar code area if it is taller. This is nothing more than saying that it's easier to hit the side of a barn than a bull's-eye. Height also takes into consideration that, while our mind tells us to scan in a straight line, our hand scans in an arc as the diagram on the next page shows.

The minimum height of a bar code for a hand-held reader is .25 inches or 15 percent of the length of the symbol, whichever is greater. The minimum height for a fixed scanner is .80 inches or 25 percent of the symbol length, whichever is greater.

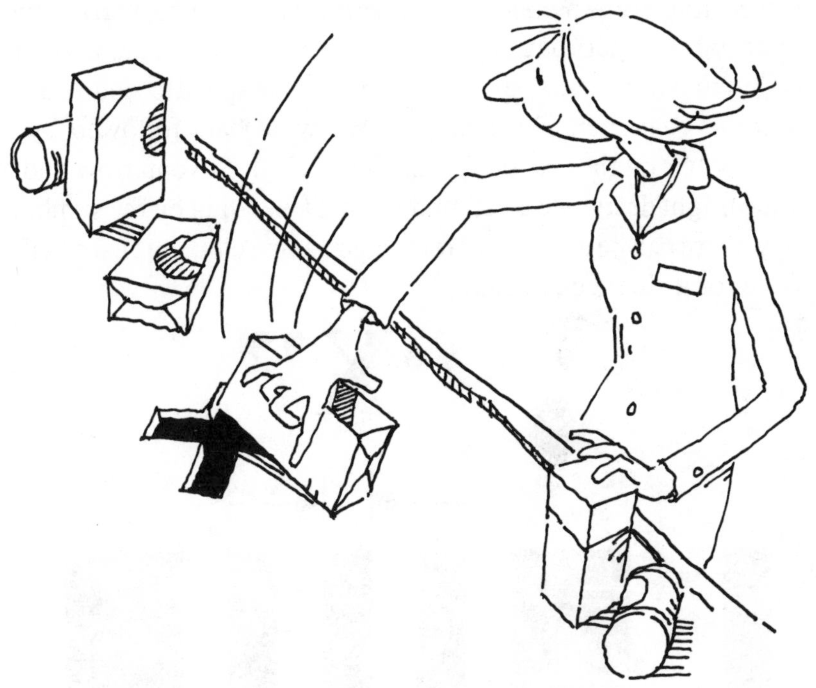

Avoid "Curved" Scans

Of course, there are limits to how tall a bar code can be and still fit on the product and retain its print quality. Often, when a bar code must fit on an object as small as a computer chip, for example, fixed readers would be our choice over hand-held devices. For such a product, there is a need to select a symbology which allows for decreased heights.

The next specification to consider is the ***width*** of the narrowest element of the bar code. This width is referred to as the "X" dimension.

Other elements of the code are often a multiple of the "X"

dimension. Some symbologies have only two widths, narrow and wide, while others have up to eighteen. Some combination of the different widths and spaces make up the specific code for a specific character. For example, two wide bars followed by a narrow bar might encode for the numeral "1," two narrow and a wide might designate a "2," and so on. Depending on the symbology, there can be anywhere from three to nine elements used in the code for a single character.

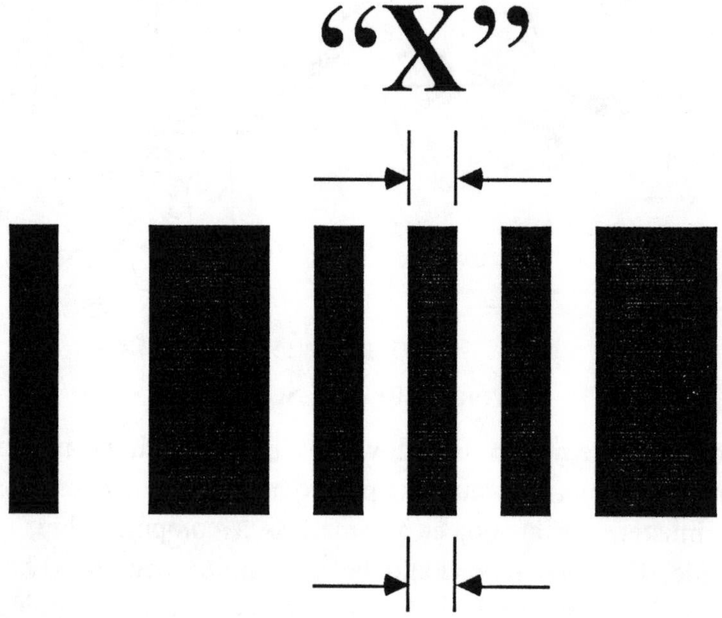

The "X" Dimension

The encoding of characters by specific combinations of wide and narrow bars and spaces and the "X" dimension account for the **density** of the symbology. Density is important to the eventual application of a bar code. Density refers to the number of characters which can be encoded in a given unit of length. It is usually expressed as the number of characters per inch. A symbology with a high density allows more information to be encoded in a smaller area. High density codes would be better suited to products where the label must be smaller in area in order to fit.

Different Densities of Code 39 and UPC

Depending on your application, you also have the choice between choosing a symbology which is only **numeric** or one that is **alphanumeric**. Although not always a primary consideration for selection, it can be easier to adapt existing part numbers to alphanumeric. An alphanumeric symbology can reflect the mnemonic qualities of part numbers or departments. For example, material for the Engineering department might be preceded by the prefix "ENG," Purchasing by "PUR," etc. Symbologies such as Code 39 will allow you to retain these prefixes.

Another feature of bar coding structure which will influence your choice of symbology also can make it easier for you to implement bar coding. Symbologies, such as UPC, are **fixed** in length. In other words, you can only use a set number of characters in any bar code label you might create. If the fixed length is eight characters, then all the items you bar code must have an identification number which is exactly eight characters long. If they are currently ten characters long, two characters must be taken off. If they are four characters long, four characters must be added. In a start-up situation, this may not be a disadvantage since you will be able to assign part numbers of eight characters right from the beginning. Often, however, companies have an identification system where part numbers are of **variable** length. Fortunately, there is Code 39 for which you are able to use as many characters as are needed for your application.

Bar code symbologies are also **continuous** or **discrete**. This feature becomes particularly important where printing is concerned. Continuous codes treat the information in a label as one unit, so they must be printed as a unit. This means that you will not be able to use all types of conventional printers, but may have to rely on the preparation of film masters. For applications where the information does not change often or one label is applied to a large number of items, this should present no problem. Discrete codes have **intercharacter gaps**. Thus, you can use conventional printers or typewriters to print out the label. This is advantageous in environments where there are many unique labels to be printed.

The last feature of symbologies which we will discuss is **self-checking**, the ability of the code to guard against undetected errors. Depending on their structure, symbologies have differing checking abilities. Some codes need to add a **check character** to strengthen their checking and reduce the number of errors. You should be aware that a check character will increase the length of your label. This may be a consideration if the space available for the label is limited.

In Chapter 1, we talked about read rates. These are also an important feature of bar coding systems. They indicate the "user-friendliness" of the system. We mentioned that the **first read rate**, the ratio of the number of successful reads to the number of attempted reads, should be at least 95% in order to reduce the frustration of users. Every new idea, system or technique meets with an initial reluctance. If users feel that the bar code reader is not doing the job correctly or too slowly, then their acceptance of the entire system will be slow. The first read rate does not only depend on the capabilities of bar code readers and their users. The print quality of the label and how that matches the capability of the reader also determines the readability of the code.

In addition to read rates, we should also consider the **substitution error rate** of bar code systems. This is the ratio of the number of incorrect characters to the total number of entered characters. For the most part, error rates are low (up to one incorrect character for every 70,000,000 entries) because of the self-checking features of most symbologies.

WHY SO MANY SYMBOLOGIES

Why are there so many symbologies? Over 100 at the last count. It's like asking why are there French, Spanish and English? Or, why is "A" the first letter of the alphabet? Some people somewhat facetiously blame the abundance of symbologies on the engineers for what appears to be a Tower of Babel. There is, however, a grain of truth to this explanation.

The Bar Code Tower of Babel

Most symbologies were developed by people working for companies who were trying to apply bar coding to a specific problem. They did so long before there were any standards. So, if one company wanted a bar code to identify vats of chemicals and another company wanted a bar code to identify boxes of candy, each went out and developed its own symbology. This is simplifying the situation to some extent. There were symbologies around which were gaining in popularity, but it took some time and experimentation to develop a symbology that was both flexible and useful.

STANDARDIZATION

After the birth of bar coding, the next most significant event was the advent of standardization in the industry. In fact, standardization is probably the single most important factor in the growth of bar coding. Standardization has also made easier the task of choosing the best symbology for a specific application. Many times, the best choice has already been made for you. If you are in the grocery industry, for example, the present standard is the Universal Product Code (UPC), the same code we see on loaves of bread. Thus it makes sense to find out first what your industry is already employing.

It also makes sense to use the standard to its fullest. In grocery stores, for example, UPC is primarily used to record the price of the customer's groceries and not always for the control and replenishment of inventory. Companies which use bar coding should endeavor to take advantage of all of its applications in order to better manage their business.

Bar code standards break down into two areas:

> **Symbology standards** — define the manner in which information is encoded and the physical specifications of the code itself.
>
> **Application or content standards** — define how the reader or the system interprets the message in the code.

To give you an idea of how complex these standards are, we have listed the sections contained in an Automotive Industry Action Group (AIAG) publication for The Code 3-of-9 symbology:

Code 3 of 9 Standards Outline

1. Scope
2. Definitions
3. 3-of-9 Bar Code
    - 3.1 General Description
    - 3.2 Code Configuration
    - 3.3 Code Density and Dimensions
    - 3.4 Bar and Space Width Tolerances
    - 3.5 Human-Readable Interpretation
    - 3.6 Additional Guidelines
        - 3.6.1 Full ASCII
        - 3.6.2 Check Digits
4. Print and Quality Assurance Requirements
    - 4.1 Reflectivity and Contrast
    - 4.2 Quiet Zone
    - 4.3 Bar Edge Roughness
    - 4.4 Quality Assurance
5. Printing Methods
    - 5.1 Bar Code Symbol Printing
    - 5.2 Film Masters
    - 5.3 Direct Printing on Corrugated Board
6. Label Materials
    - 6.1 Substrates
    - 6.2 Opacity
    - 6.3 Smoothness and Gloss

These specifications fill up an eight page pamphlet. At some point, you will need to study similar sets of specifications when choosing a symbology for your application. There are many excellent publications available for this use. The American National Standards Institute (ANSI), for example, has published a pamphlet which describes the standards for a number of bar codes in the application of materials handling (specifically, bar code symbols on unit loads and transport packages). These publications, however, presuppose that you already know what you are looking for. We have found that you cannot make this assumption. We recommend looking at the standards in your particular industry in order to avoid reinventing the wheel.

The Uniform Code Council (UCC), formerly the Uniform Product Code Council, developed and now administers the standards for the Uniform Product Code (UPC) found predominantly in the grocery industry. The institution of this standard was so successful that Europe and other countries adopted the European Article Numbering (EAN) code for a wide range of retail goods, including grocery items. The EAN now calls itself the International Article Numbering Association, reflecting the world-wide acceptance of bar coding.

In blood banking or related fields, the standard which was established by the Committee for Commonality in Blood Banking Automation (CCBBA) as the industry's symbology was Codabar.

The Department of Defense chartered the Logistics Applications of Automated Marking and Reading Systems (LOGMARS) to establish a standard for shipments from suppliers. LOGMARS selected Code 39, which the department refers to as Code 3-of-9. Certainly, if you are a defense contractor, you are already using or will soon be using this standard.

The American National Standards Institute (ANSI), which is a non-profit organization, does not work for a particular industry.

But, because of its independent status, it has gathered knowledgeable people to develop a national standard for Code 39, Interleaved 2 of 5 and Codabar. This was published in the pamphlet mentioned earlier.

The Automotive Industry Action Group (AIAG) is another nonprofit organization formed to establish standards for automakers and their suppliers. Using the expertise of members who work in the industry, standards were developed for their selection of Code 39 as the symbology for the auto industry.

Spurred on by the need to reduce costs, several health industry trade associations gathered to discuss bar coding. The result was the formation of the Health Industry Bar Code Council (HIBCC) which oversaw the establishment of Code 39. This symbology was chosen because it could best meet the many and varied needs of participants in HIBCC which includes health care manufacturers, distributors, providers and technical experts.

There are many other standardization organizations. One that deserves special mention is Automatic Identification Manufacturers (AIM) which is a trade association for bar code manufacturers. AIM's aim, one could say, is to focus on the application or content standards with the goal of creating a "generic" bar code symbology standard. They have succeeded in developing five Uniform Symbology Specifications (USS) for the five most used symbologies. The attention paid to application standards is particularly important because it has paved the way for one bar code reader to read several different codes whether by the creation of special software or hardware. Such systems are described as being **autodiscriminate**. The bar code reader is able to read up to eleven different symbologies and automatically decode the label being scanned. In a sense, we have got around the "why so many symbologies" Tower of Babel by becoming multilingual.

HOW TO SELECT A SYMBOLOGY

What must be kept in mind when you select a symbology is that the features a company desires may conflict with each other. For example, you may want a bar code with a high density and data security. The extra characters needed for improved security can work against the need for a smaller label which is answered by a symbology with high density. You will definitely be trading off conflicting properties as you make your choice. You not only have to keep in mind what is the best code for the application, but how that code fits with other internal operations and with the external world of suppliers and customers. What would you do, for example, if your company was better served by an alphanumeric code while your suppliers and customers use a numeric only code? Obviously, there will be a need to analyze the benefits and costs of each alternative. To help you, we have devised the following guidelines in selecting a symbology. They will help you weigh the different features of various symbologies against each other.

1. Industry Standard — Is your industry already using a standard symbology?

We mentioned earlier that selecting an industry standard can help you avoid reinventing the wheel. In many instances, significant amounts of thought have gone into the selection of a particular symbology. It is to your benefit to take advantage of this accumulated expertise, but it does not mean that you are obligated to choose the standard exclusively. Many companies are able to use two or more symbologies now that bar code systems are "multilingual."

2. Character Sets — Does the symbology incorporate all the characters currently used in your company?

In this category, you will first need to know the present criteria for information within the company. Obviously, alphanumeric information will strongly weigh in favor of choosing a symbology with an alphanumeric character set.

3. Accuracy — Does the symbology have a level of accuracy or self-checking which is adequate for your application?

In the banking industry or health care industry, for example, there is no room for error. Certain symbologies have a self-checking feature which is inherent to the structure. For example, 2 of 5 Code contains a character set where each character must have two wide and three narrow bars. Any other combination would not make a valid character. This may affect other features, such as density or character set, but if accuracy is vital to the application, then you will need to choose among those symbologies which are resistant to errors.

4. Density — Does the symbology allow you to create and print a label with all the necessary information?

Some symbologies have a higher density and thus lend themselves to applications where small labels are required for small parts. Computer chips are an obvious example. Conversely, it may be necessary for a label to be large, as is the case with corrugated packing cartons. Larger labels are easier to read by both human operators or by scanners on a production line.

5. Tolerances — Does the symbology have specifications which will make it difficult for you to hold to tolerances?

This category is influenced by the structural characteristics of the symbology. Structural simplicity makes it easier to print and read bar codes. UPC, for example, has four different specifications for bar and space widths. Codabar has eighteen. This may present a problem if you intend to print the labels in-house.

Every symbology has a specification sheet which indicates the minimum and maximum tolerances for a printed symbol. Obviously, a symbology with more degrees of latitude will make it less difficult for you to fall within this range. At least 90% of the problems with bar coding result from poorly printed or maintained labels. This will mean that readers and scanners must be capable of holding to the same printing tolerances as the printers.

FEATURES OF STANDARD SYMBOLOGIES

2 of 5 CODE

The 2 of 5 Code has a total of five bars—two wide and three narrow. All narrow bars are called the "x" dimension and have to be the same width. The wide bars are a width factor of the narrow bars (between two to four times as thick).

In the airlines industry, each piece of baggage for a particular flight has a predetermined code that routes the suitcase down on a system of automatic conveyors to the exact gate where the departing airplane waits. The 2 of 5 Code lends itself to similar applications in which routing and sortation are important. Generally, the 2 of 5 Code is an easy system to implement and is a good choice when only a minimal amount of information needs to be encoded.

Applications:

- Warehouse inventory handling.
- Identifying photofinishing envelopes.
- Airline ticketing.
- Baggage and cargo handling.

2 of 5 Code

Features:

- Numeric characters only.
- Discrete and self-checking.
- Easy to print and read.
- Relatively low density.
- Easy to decode.

INTERLEAVED 2 OF 5 (I 2 of 5)

The spaces in Interleaved 2 of 5 are used as white bars which makes this symbology twice as dense (17.8 characters/inch) as the 2 of 5 Code. Couple this feature with the fact that Interleaved 2 of 5 is both easy to print and read and the result is a symbology that has become the standard for labeling corrugated cartons. In the cigarette industry, for example, the cartons and packs sold at stores carry a UPC label but the corrugated carton that they are shipped in carries an Interleaved 2 of 5 label. This symbology's use as an identifier on shipping containers of all types cuts across every industry. It is highly likely, then, that you will choose Interleaved 2 of 5 for your own shipping applications, especially if you will be printing on corrugated cartons. Although there is a tendency to obtain partial reads of the entire label as a valid message, this problem can be cleared up with the use of fixed symbol lengths and the presence of a check digit. Also, the code must be an even number of characters in length or you must add a leading zero.

Applications:

- Warehouses.
- Heavy industries.
- Automotive — corrugated shipping containers.
- Grocery — shipping boxes.

Interleaved 2 of 5

Features:

- Numeric only.
- Continuous.
- Self-checking.
- Relatively high density.
- Easy to print and decode.
- Requires even number of characters.
- Tendency for foreshortened reads and substitution errors.
- Data integrity enhanced by fixed field size.
- Data integrity enhanced by adding two-character check digit.

CODE 39

Code 39 has nine bars, three wide and six narrow. The bars are made up of both light bars (spaces) and dark bars. Code 39 is the symbology that the majority of users will select. It is widely used with other standards in a company because it allows for alphabetic information. It has also been selected as the standard symbology by LOGMARS, AIAG and HIBCC.

Code 39 is commonly used to track inventory within a facility or distribution center. As material travels in and out of storerooms and around the shop floor, there is a need to track data. For example, lots on the floor are accompanied by a traveling document which contains information such as the work order number, the lot's present location, its destination, start and completion dates, and quantity. Each of these areas has its own distinct field. An operator is then able to wand the document, package or part after selecting a bar code for a particular operation on a menu which sits at the work station. Here is an excellent example of the capacity for bar coding to supply accurate, real-time information about operations on a shop floor.

Applications:

- Automotive.
- Department of Defense.
- Government.
- Healthcare.
- Manufacturing.
- Hospitals.
- Universities.
- Government.

Features:

- Discrete and self-checking.
- Alphanumeric.

- Full ASCII capability (character set).
- Easy to print.
- High level of acceptance in the bar code industry.
- Considered to be very accurate with a high immunity to substitution errors.

CODABAR

Research done by the Committee for Commonality in Blood Banking Automation (CCBBA) task force suggests that Codabar is capable of a first pass read of 99 percent and substitution error rate of 1 in 1,000,000 reads without a check digit and 1 in 1,000,000,000 with a check digit. Codabar is an excellent symbology for applications where accuracy is a critical factor. It is uniquely qualified for the purposes of identifying or tracking which is why the blood banking industry and Federal Express have selected it. However, you will rarely see this symbology used in manufacturing environments, principally because it is more difficult to print and not alphanumeric. Only the first and last digit can be an "A" through "D"; the other characters must be numeric.

Those companies who do use Codabar typically buy the system as a package in which the labels are manufactured and printed by professional printers. This is fine when you know what your labels needs are beforehand so that they can be sequentially numbered. This is not the case on a shop floor where labels do not necessarily follow in numerical order, but where they contain information which is unique to a certain job or lot. Since most manufacturers use dot matrix printers, it is difficult to hold to Codabar's printing tolerances.

Applications:

- Blood processing industry.
- Libraries.
- Federal and municipal governments.
- Universities.
- Federal Express (preprinted airbills).
- Air freight forwarders.
- Photofinishing envelopes.

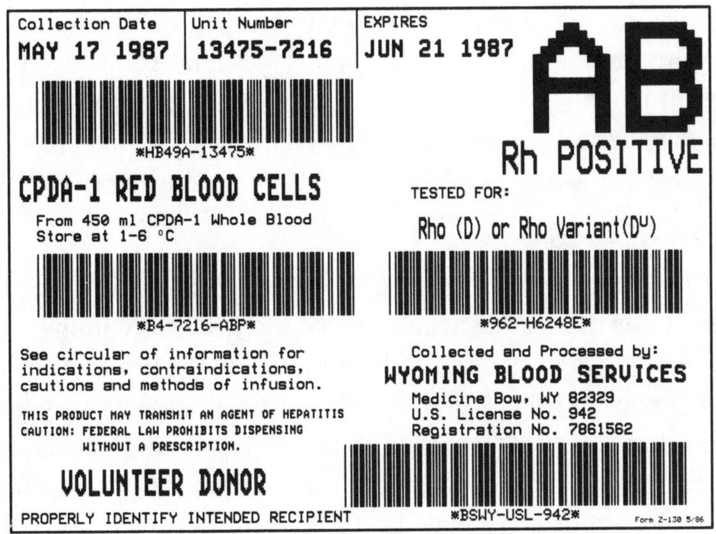

Typical Codabar Label

Features:

- Discrete and self-checking.
- Numeric with limited control characters (the letters A-D).
- Historically difficult to print because of 18 different wide/narrow ratios.

- Accepted as being very accurate.
- Ability to concatenate labels and use combinations of start/stop characters for encoding data.

UNIVERSAL PRODUCT CODE (UPC)

If you have an "after-market" for your product, you will most likely need to use UPC. Because of its predetermined length, however, this symbology has limited usefulness in the manufacturing environment. The reason for this is that labels need to be of different lengths. UPC labels are also difficult to print in-house since they have so many tolerances. At the present time, readers, like those at a grocery checkout counter, may cost up to $25,000 per station.

The first character of a UPC label is the industry classification (prescription drugs, magazines, liquor, etc.). The remaining characters contain the customer code, the code for the product and the last character is a check digit. UPC labels can initiate many tasks in one operation as the labels do at the grocery store. For example, both the price is recorded by the machine and, in some cases, inventory records are updated.

UPC's success has recently raised a problem. Numerous companies are applying for a UPC customer code making it a possibility that the code will run out of numbers. There are also a number of subsets of UPC and potential buyers of the system should be warned that not all readers can interpret all the subsets of UPC. This is true, too, for the European Article Numbering (EAN) of which UPC is a subset. All UPC readers can't read all of the characters in EAN.

Applications:

- Grocery.
- Retail stores.
- Magazines and books.
- Music industry.
- Liquor industry.

UPC Bar Code

Features:

- Continuous and self-checking.
- Check digit included.
- Acceptable data accuracy.
- Widely accepted and used in retail industry.
- Numeric only.

EUROPEAN ARTICLE NUMBERING (EAN)

The EAN is used in Europe instead of the UPC. Other than that difference, the two codes are much the same with the differences noted above in the section on UPC. Like UPC, its universal acceptance is a major feature. A product bar coded in England, for example, can be read in Italy as well.

Applications:

- Grocery.
- Retail.

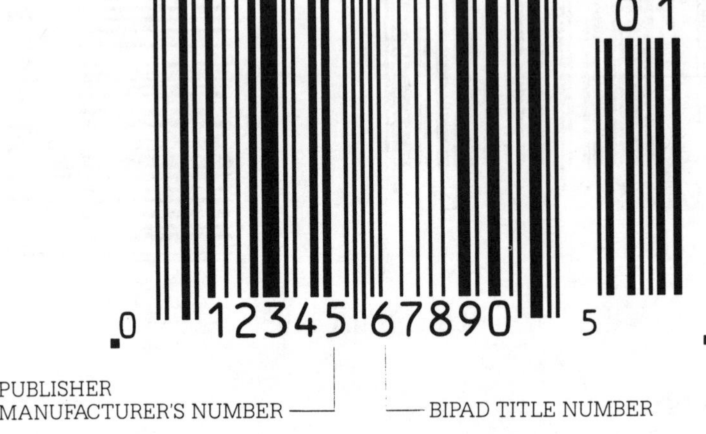

EAN Bar Code for Magazine

Features:

- Continuous.
- Check digit included.
- Country of origin digit included.
- Widely accepted and compatible with point of sale systems.
- Similar to UPC and method of encoding.
- Numeric only.

CODE 93 AND CODE 128

Both **Code 93** and **Code 128** are take-offs of Code 39 and were developed in order to gain higher density. Whereas Code 39 has a density of 9.4 characters/inch, Code 93 and Code 128 are between 12 and 24 characters/inch, depending on the alpha/ numeric mix of the characters. The more numeric characters, the higher the density. This has made it possible to encode long messages of up to 30 characters which is attractive to environments where complex instructions need to be encoded. Both codes may also be an appropriate choice if you need to make small labels. Since neither code is widely accepted, applications have been limited to internal operations or to situations where the two can complement Code 39. For the most part, scanners can read all three codes.

Code 93 Bar Code

Code 128 Bar Code

CODE 49 AND CODE 16K

Code 49 and **Code 16K** also complement Code 39, that is, readers can be programmed to read Code 39 and its complement. Both of these recently developed codes look something like crossword puzzles and were designed for high density and for labeling small products. Code 16K can stack between two and sixteen rows, while Code 49 is capable of two to eight lines. These symbologies can print between 90 and 150 characters per inch, depending again on the alpha/numeric mix.

Each row itself is a conventional symbol, but it also contains information about its position in the stack. The entire stack also contains check characters and coding which indicates the number of rows in the whole symbol. This information allows the reader to know when all the rows have been read, so that it can give a "beep" indicating that there has been a good read. Stacked codes are also designed so that all the rows do not have to be read in order. Thus, if one or more rows is missed in the first scan, they can be read again on another scan.

Typical Code 49 and Code 16K Symbols

CIRCULAR BAR CODE

The last code of significance is the **Circular Bar Code** or the Bull's Eye which was developed for cylindrical products. The code is placed on top of the product so that it can be read in any orientation as the cylinders come down a production line.

CONCLUSIONS ABOUT SYMBOLOGIES

Bar codes are used for the following basic applications:

1. Sorting.
2. Routing.
3. Identification.
4. Tracking.
5. Inventory counts.

What is interesting about this list is that it pertains equally well to distributors, retailers and manufacturers. Whatever the business, these basic concerns are identical. That is part of the power of bar coding which allows a company to gain control of operations. But, no company can expect to gain this control merely by implementing bar coding. Business needs must be analyzed, basic disciplines put in place and a sense of direction instilled in the company before bar coding can reach its potential.

There are two basic questions to ask when selecting a bar code:

1. Has your industry already chosen a standard symbology?
2. Do you need a numeric or an alphanumeric symbology?

The following chart compares the features of the standard symbologies discussed in this chapter:

COMPARISON OF SELECTED SYMBOLOGIES

	I 2 of 5	Code39	Codabar	UPC	Code 128
Development Date	1972	1974	1972	1973	1981
Specification Standard	AIM ANSI	AIM ANSI	CCBBA ANSI	UPCC IAN	AIM
Application Area	Industry	Industry	Medical	Retail	Industry
Variable Length	No	Yes	Yes	No	Yes
Alphanumeric	No	Yes	No	No	Yes
Discrete	No	Yes	Yes	No	No
Self-Checking	Yes	Yes	Yes	Yes	Yes
Density (Char/In.)	17.8	9.4	12	12	24.2
Data Security	High	High	High	Medium	High

At present, there is a shaking out in the bar coding industry of symbologies. It is similar to what the computer industry faced with programming languages. Languages which were developed before standardization were still in use even though superior languages were later created. It was costly to change a company's system over from the old language to the new or from an old computer system to a more recent one. In the application of the bar coding by various industries, we also see pockets where less popular symbologies are still used. Even so, UPC and Code 39 now account for approximately 90-95 percent of the market. Add the use of I 2 of 5 for corrugated cartons and these three symbologies account for approximately 98 percent of the applications of bar codes.

Those who are now entering the world of bar coding for the first time choose Code 39. It has become an industry standard and is also becoming the choice of major retail chains, such as KMart, WalMart and others, as they switch over from Optical Character Recognition to bar coding.

This does not mean that Code 39 is the only choice for you or that it will be the only symbology you will use. However, there is a trend toward the narrowing of choices. Only specialized industries which already have a standard will be the exceptions. Such an industry is blood banking which has settled on Codabar. As we have said earlier, there is no best symbology. The best symbology depends on how you will use it and the business applications.

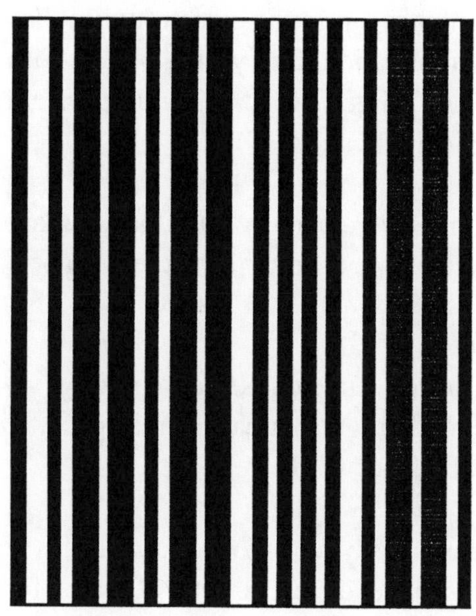

CHAPTER THREE: Bar Code Printing

This chapter begins discussing the elements of a bar coding system and how to implement them. Implementation is an effort in balancing the demands of the application with the capabilities of the various elements. For example, you may already have dot matrix printers at your site and will probably want to decrease costs by adapting the bar coding system to their capabilities. This may or may not work, depending in part on the size of the label and how dense the symbology must be. Laser or thermal printers may be the only viable alternatives for this application. In that case, you will either have to buy new printers or rethink your application.

In short, a company cannot choose a printing system until it has clearly defined the system's application. Everything begins with the application. There is no best printer; only the printing system which is best for your specific application.

Whatever the application, however, certain variables remain constant. Every printing system must be able to create labels which can do the following:

1. Hold to the tolerances of the chosen symbology.
2. Allow scanners to distinguish a bar from a space.
3. Print free of ink blobs or voids.

As can be seen, these variables directly relate to the capabilities of scanners. Different scanners have different sets of rules for decoding the bars and spaces on a label. Some scanners, for instance, are more forgiving than others. They are able to read labels printed by less accurate methods. If you know which printer and scanner you will be using, you will be better able to create a system with less reading errors. However, if you print labels for products which are shipped to customers and don't know which scanners are used, this can present problems. As with all systems, knowing what your customer wants is of paramount importance. Whenever possible, you should find out whether their scanners can read what your printing system produces.

A substantial majority of the problems in bar coding is the result of bad labels, either because they were not properly printed or not properly protected after they were attached to the product. It pays, then, not to take short-cuts when selecting and buying printing systems. A great many bar coding problems can be eliminated by producing labels of high quality.

Printing systems are also dependent on the symbology chosen. Certain symbologies cannot be printed except by high resolution printers. Here, too, is another variable to weigh in the implementation equation for printing systems.

SELECTING A PRINTING METHOD

Before discussing the features of several printing systems, let's review two methods of obtaining bar code labels. The first is on-site printing where the company creates the labels it needs. On-site printing can be done in batches if the company already knows what information the labels will hold or printing can be done on demand if labels are created only as needed. The second method is off-site printing which is simply the creation of bar code labels at a commercial printer. Again, the advantages and disadvantages of each depend upon your application.

There are several questions to ask before selecting one of these methods:

1. Which is most cost-effective?
2. Which method provides the needed quality or resolution?
3. Do you need to print short or long runs? Is the process discrete or repetitive?

4. Are the labels predetermined or made to demand?
5. Is the commercial printer able to meet your requirements?
6. What is the lead time for delivery of labels from a commercial printer?
7. What issues are there with storage and inventory?
8. How does flexible manufacturing technology fit with the label creation process?

COMPARISON OF PRINTING SYSTEMS

A number of different print technologies have been used to print bar codes. These technologies roughly break down into two categories: impact and non-impact printing techniques. Impact printing includes dot matrix and drum (or formed character) printers. Non-impact printing includes thermal direct, thermal transfer, electrostatic (laser printers), laser etching and ink jet printers. According to a recent survey conducted by Frost & Sullivan, a leading provider of automation studies in the United States and Europe, user preference is as illustrated on the opposite page.

Before we look at the features and applications of each of the printing technologies listed above, let's briefly define each .

Dot matrix printers form characters when a printing head, consisting of an array of pins, is activated by software. The impact of these pins on an inked ribbon prints the image on the paper.

Drum or **formed-character** printers have reversed images of bars etched on the surface of a rotating drum. The image is

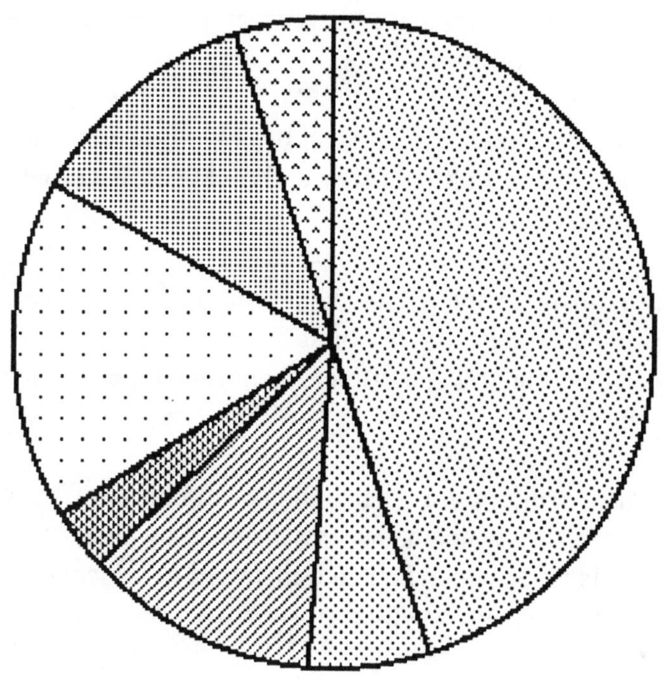

Printer Type	% of Users
Dot Matrix	45 %
Formed Character	6 %
Ink Jet	12 %
Electrostatic	3 %
Laser Etching	17 %
Thermal	12 %
Thermal Transfer	5 %

transferred to the paper when a hammer strikes the paper and the ribbon against the drum.

Thermal direct printers form images by heating different areas of the printing head which cause special, heat-sensitive paper to record the character or bar.

Thermal transfer printers also have printing heads which heat up, but use a heat-sensitive ribbon in order to impress the image onto paper. Thermal transfer printers do not need special, thermal sensitive paper.

Electrostatic printers use a technology similar to office copy machines. A drum, which has been sensitized by a moving laser beam, attracts toner which is then transferred to a sheet of paper which comes into contact with the drum.

Laser etchers actually "burn" the desired image into the item being bar coded or "burn off" a special coating so that the item's surface is exposed.

Ink jet printers are similar to dot matrix printers. Instead of a pin being pressed against a ribbon, however, controlled jets of ink are sprayed from small nozzles to form the image.

PRINT SYSTEMS: FEATURES AND APPLICATIONS

DOT MATRIX

Dot matrix printers are the most popular printing devices used in bar coding systems today because they are inexpensive and

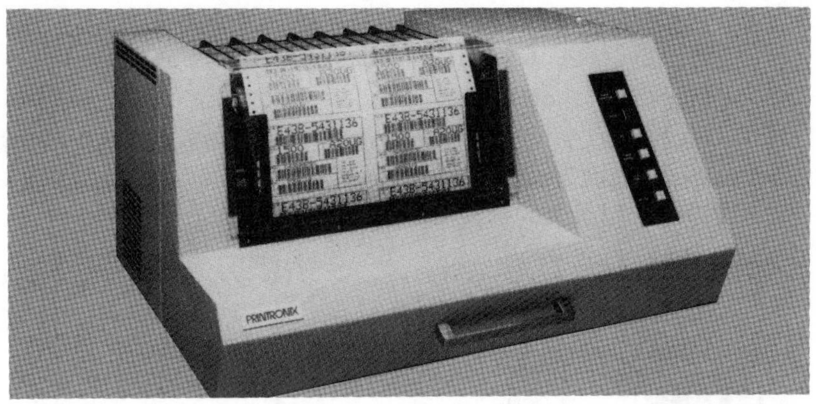

Dot Matrix Printer

Photo Courtesy of Printronix

flexible. Dot matrix printers can be purchased for under $1,000, although models specifically designed for bar coding are more expensive. Such printers produce a higher quality label, but they should not be used for applications other than bar coding. Versatility, however, has been one of the major reasons why dot matrix printers are so popular. They not only can print bar code labels, but human-readable text and graphics as well. There is a cost for such flexibility. If the dot matrix printer is shared with other applications, it will be harder to obtain the level of quality needed to assure good reads.

Dot matrix printers are an excellent choice for putting bar codes on computerized reports and forms. Printers are already available on the factory floor or in the office. Putting them to another use will double their usefulness. Bar codes are easily printed on computerized reports and forms for inventory shortages, purchase order look-ups, shop floor documents, receiving documents, shipping papers, etc. Some creativity must be employed to get around the problem of multiple copies on these reports. Bar codes are not readable when they are produced by the carbon sheets of multi-formed reports. There are two easy solutions. One, print the bar code on every sheet in a non-carbonized area or, two, make a step-laddered form with the bar code at the bottom of each sheet.

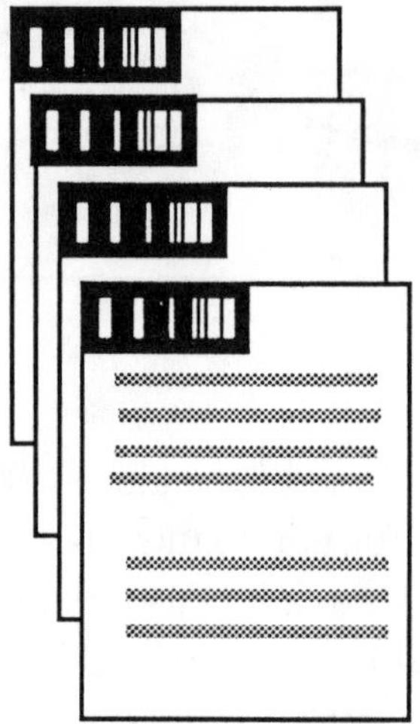

Solution 1: Bar codes on non-carbonized areas.

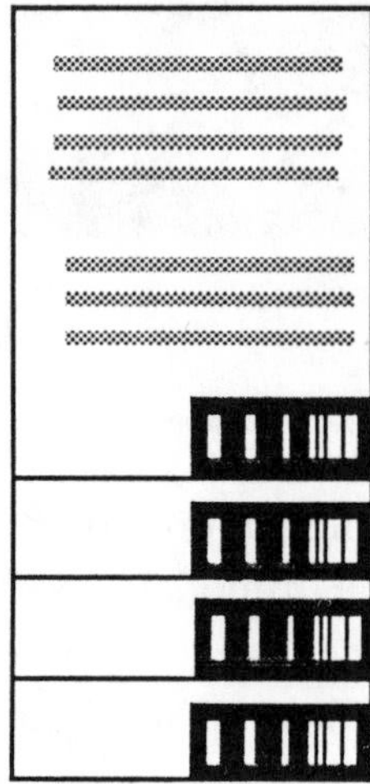

Solution 2: Bar codes on step-laddered form.

In general, dot matrix printers are good for low to medium volume applications. Most printers are capable of 30-200 labels per minute. Dot matrix printers work best with a symbology which is tolerant (resistant to lower print quality) and with labels of a larger size. Dot matrix printers are not capable of high densities. The typical number of characters per inch is three to five. The exception is six to seven. Therefore, even if the chosen symbology allows higher densities, the printer won't allow it. This may mean choosing an electrostatic or thermal printer or changing symbologies. It's a trade-off which can only be decided by assessing the company's business requirements. In other words, is it possible to use a bigger label and thus print with a dot matrix?

Some of the quality problems with dot matrix printers can be solved by using higher quality ribbons which produce images that do not bleed or have ragged edges. There are also dot matrix printers with 24 pins instead of the usual seven to nine. The dot matrix print element consists of a series of pins arranged in an array. These pins strike an inked ribbon and produce a series of dots on the printed material. The bar code symbol is built up from these lines of dots. A narrow bar code is created by printing a set of overlapping dots. Wider bars are printed by overlapping narrow bars.

Another factor to consider when implementing a bar coding system using a dot matrix printer is the durability of the image. How many times will the operator scan the label? A contact reader destroys the readability of the label after 50 scans. One way to circumvent this problem is to print the bar code symbol more than once on the form or product. For example, if a work order number on a report were to be scanned 120 times, the bar code symbol may have to be printed three times.

The environment in which the bar code label exists needs to be assessed as well. Will it be subject to sunlight or extreme heat? If so, the ink may fade and make the label unreadable. Determine the shelf-life of the label and how environmental conditions will affect the label over time.

Dot matrix printers often produce a negative reaction because users claim that their scanners can't read the label after a short period of time or use. The fact is, however, that most people forget to change the ribbon. A label printed by a ribbon going around for the second or third time is going to decrease in print quality. Ribbons must be scheduled and changed as part of a preventive maintenance program. One manufacturer of printers has solved this problem by counting the number of lines you have printed and alerting the user to when the ribbon needs to be changed. Although used ribbons may not be good enough for printing bar codes, they can be used for other applications. We know of one company which routes ribbons back to the MIS department in order to squeeze out the remaining 30 percent of the ribbon's life. At $2.50-15.00 per ribbon, this is not an insignificant amount. It also points out the need to look for hidden costs when implementing a bar coding system. Many companies overlook the cost of supplies when implementing a system.

DRUM (FORMED CHARACTER) PRINTERS

Drum Printer

Drum printers produce bar codes of high reliability and outstanding quality. They can print 40 to 100 labels per minute and are good for medium volume and high resolution applications. A minor drawback is that they tend to be noisy which may limit their use in the office. The major drawback is that they are limited to only printing the symbology engraved on the drum and only in that size. In order to print another symbology, you would need another drum. To change the height of a bar code would also mean switching printing heads. These drawbacks limit the number of applications for which drum printers are useful.

These same features, however, do make this type of printer a good choice for applications where sequential bar codes must be printed. A company that manufactures the same product or type of product daily will have a use for this type of printer. Such companies would be in the cosmetics, food or tobacco industries like Cosmair, General Foods and Phillip Morris. In the food industry, for example, product change-overs are from one flavor to another and do not require a change in label size.

It is possible to define fields on the label which can be either incremented or decremented. This capacity makes drum printers useful for automatic identification applications such as employee badges, file folder labeling, tool crib systems, picking systems or shelf labeling.

THERMAL PRINTERS

Thermal printers (also known as thermal direct and heat stamp) are inexpensive and produce high quality labels. They are also very quiet in their operation and thus are ideal for offices, libraries or hospitals. They have two disadvantages, however. They print at a relatively low speed and use special, heat-sensitive paper which is more expensive than paper stock used for other printers.

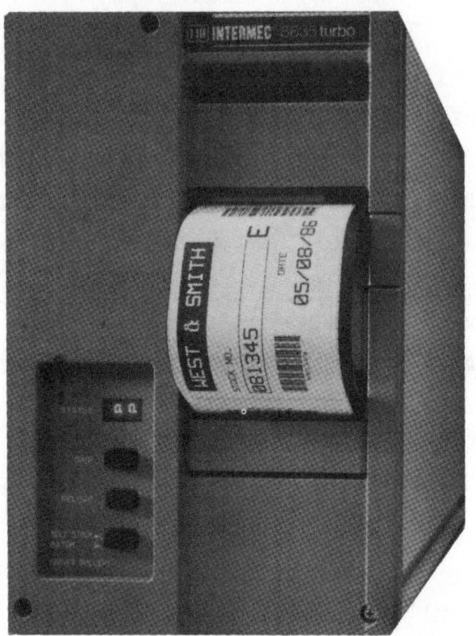

Thermal Printer

Photo Courtesy of Intermec

This special paper also limits the life cycle of bar codes printed with thermal printers. Although some in the industry claim that the shelf life of a thermally printed label is one to three years, our experience is that it is much less. In fact, on one receiving dock in Phoenix, Arizona, we watched as labels turned completely black in less than eight hours. Temperatures over 140 degrees, some industrial lighting and sunlight will darken the paper. There are newer paper products which address some of these problems, but at a higher cost.

Besides being careful about a label fading, you also need to be concerned about which reader you choose to scan. Not all laser readers will be able to obtain a readable scan since there is not enough contrast in the infrared range of light.

THERMAL TRANSFER PRINTERS

Along with electrostatic or laser printers, thermal transfer printers are becoming the choice of a majority of bar code users since the printers produce labels of outstanding quality. Ink is transferred to the paper by means of a heating element striking a ribbon, the ink dries on contact and is not subject to darkening or fading from sunlight or heat. Bar codes printed by thermal transfer printers are durable and won't smudge. Printers are also quiet and suitable for environments where noise may be a factor.

Thermal Transfer Printer

Photo Courtesy of Intermec

Thermal transfer printers are capable of printing 25-100 labels per minute at present, but this number is constantly improving. Printers can also be programmed for more than one printing font which allows for a variety of applications and symbologies. Another point which gives great flexibility is the ability of thermal transfer printers to print labels on ordinary paper, including preprinted forms. The outstanding quality which is the result of the transfer process also makes it possible to print bar codes of high density. In addition, the cost of thermal transfer printing system has been coming down.

One cost, however, which must still be considered is the price of ribbons. With most thermal transfer printers, the ribbon and paper move together. This insures high quality since a character is only printed from a part of the ribbon with fresh ink. If a four-inch label is printed, four inches of ribbon will be used even though the bar code itself may only be one inch long. That's three inches of unused space on the ribbon, a 75 percent loss of the ribbon's application.

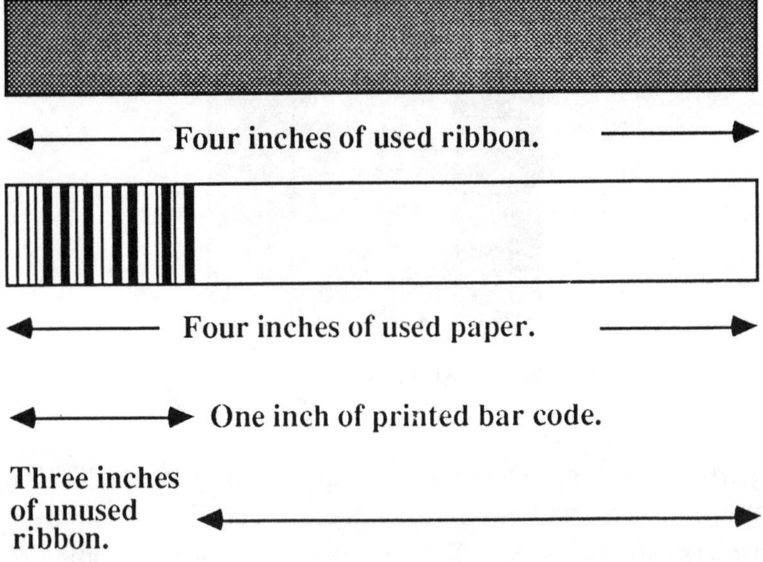

Fortunately, thermal transfer printers are now being manufactured which only advance the ribbon when a character has been printed. Thus, if you have a 40-yard roll of labels and a 40-yard ribbon, the paper will run out before the ribbon. Before, you would have to change the ribbon along with the paper.

The choice between using a laser printer or a thermal transfer printer comes down to what surface is being printed on. Since laser printers are sheet fed, they are inefficient for printing one label. Thermal transfer printers, on the other hand, are excellent for this type of application. Laser printers are better used for the printing of bar code labels on computerized forms such as purchase orders. Lasers make it possible to print the form and the bar code in the same process, thus eliminating one step.

ELECTROSTATIC (LASER) PRINTERS

Electrostatic or ion decomposition printing is a non-contact, multi-step process. Patterns of electrostatic images are charged on to the surface of a drum. Particles of ink, called toner, are attracted to the charged areas and this develops the image of the bar code on the drum. The ink image is then transferred from the drum to the paper. These areas are then fixed permanently by pressure rollers or heat. The process is similar to an office copier, but no master or photocopied image is required.

Electrostatic printers use no moving parts to print the bar code symbol which makes printing very fast. They typically operate at 400-800 inches per minute, regardless of the amount of printing on the label. Electrostatic printing also allows almost unrestricted print sizes, shapes and orientation.

Printing speeds are 125 feet per minute for cut sheets and up to 155 feet per minute for continuous forms. Almost any variety of media is acceptable — paper, vinyl label stock , foil, polyester, heavy card stock, etc.

Laser printers that are used with a personal computer are also a version of the office copier. Unfortunately, these printers are, at present, only designed for single page printing. To avoid jamming the single sheets, butt-cut rather than die-cut bar code labels should be used. The average print rate is 8 pages per minute, but some units can print at page rates of 20 per minute.

Laser and electrostatic printers produce high quality bar codes and are able to print symbologies with a high density. Care must be taken when using these printers for applications in which the label is backed with an adhesive. The heat used in the process of printing can "melt" the glue and cause jamming which may lead to expensive repairs.

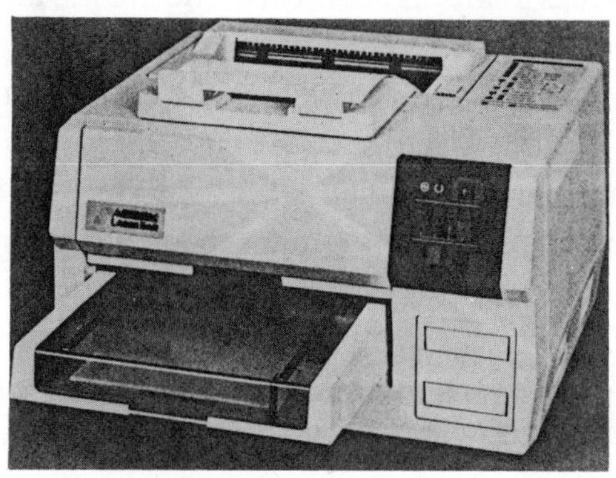

Laser Printer

Photo Courtesy of Aedex

As noted above, electrostatic printers are an excellent choice when there is need for other text or graphics (such as a computerized report) to appear on the page with the bar code. Since they are sheet-fed, however, they are best for low-volume application. It is estimated that one sheet processed by a laser printer costs 3.5 cents. To print one label per page at that price is not only inefficient, but expensive for high volumes. Another cost to take into consideration is that each toner cartridge has a life of approximately 3,000 sheets before it must be replaced. Printed bar codes which exceed that lifespan will not have enough reflectivity to record good reads.

LASER ETCHING

Bar codes formed by the laser etching process are virtually indestructible which makes them ideal for hostile environments, very long shelf-life and for items which require permanent labels which do not change. Laser etchers are expensive, from a low of $30,000 for a system to a high of $100,000 depending on the speed of the etching process which can reach as high as 48,000 pieces per hour. The key features of laser etching are its permanence and high resolution.

There are two types of laser etchers. One burns the bar code directly into the metal, plastic or wood of the item being etched. The other soft burns through a label or coating to the surface of the item. The coating which is burned away corresponds to the spaces of a bar code, while the remaining coating becomes the bars. One tire manufacturer is pushing the technology still further by experimenting with etching bar codes on tires. Although this is a black on black bar code, scanners are reading the different amounts of light being reflected back. Such scanners which are, in effect, reading shadows, are much more sophisticated than ordinary readers and, of course, more expensive.

INK JET PRINTERS

Ink jet printers are non-contact. Therefore, they can print on objects of many different contours and surface textures. They have been used to put bar codes on everything from bottles, forms, cartons to cans. Because they can print up to 2,000 characters per minute, they are ideal for automated conveyor systems (where they are usually found). However, when they are used to print on corrugated cartons, you must be aware that the ink can blob or run on the porous surfaces. This can be avoided by chemically treating the area before spraying on the bar code or having your supplier of boxes and cartons treat the cardboard.

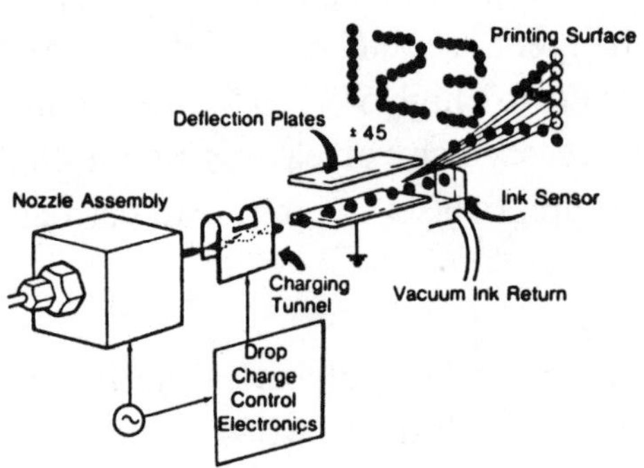

Ink Jet Printer

Although they are initially more expensive than other printing systems, ink jet printers eliminate the need for label or paper stock and thus lower ongoing costs. Although the quality of the bar code is improving, they are less reliable than other printing systems and cannot print high density bar codes.

Two types of systems are available: continuous stream and drop on demand. In the continuous stream system, the drops of ink are constantly projected toward the label surface. An electrode electrostatically deflects the drops away from the paper into a gutter for reuse. When an image is desired, the drops of ink are allowed to flow past the gutter to be deposited on the paper. The bar code symbols are formed by the dots which build up. Only 2 percent of the ink actually reaches the paper; 98 percent is recirculated. With the drop on demand system, an array of nozzles project the ink on the paper only when needed. There is no need for recirculation.

OFF-SITE PRINTING CHOICES

All commercial printing methods rely on photographic images, or film masters of high accuracy, to print bar codes. Of the printing methods, **offset lithography** provides the highest quality and density on a number of different materials. This flexibility also extends to the fact that offset presses are the most widely used presses by printing companies. Thus, you can be certain of finding a capable printer in your area. Offset lithography also is the best printing method for combining color with your bar code as it may appear on decorative packaging.

Another printing method is known as **flexographic**. The primary benefit of flexographic printing is that the ink dries very rapidly. This means you can use it for applications where you will need to print on smooth, nonabsorbent materials such as foils, films, fabrics and plastics.

Silk screening is a third commercial printing method. It is also used for a variety of materials and has the advantage of being easily printed on irregular surfaces such as plastic bottles.

Hot stamping is a slow printing method, but produces images of high quality. It is principally used for multicolored, high quality bar codes.

Letterpress printing is also produces high quality images. Its principal benefit is that its images have a durability which can last for decades.

SUPPLIER (External) VS. PLANT (Internal) PRINTING

One of the major questions to answer when implementing a bar coding system is whether to go with an internal printing system or an external supplier . ***Quality*** and ***cost*** are the two most important factors in this decision. The question boils down to this: External printing may be cheaper for long runs and may provide higher quality, but it does not allow the on-demand flexibility that on-site printing provides. The answer depends on your application. The following chart illustrates the advantages and disadvantages of each:

	PLANT (Internal)	SUPPLIER (External)
INFORMATION	Able to print unique information, (e.g., lot numbers), on demand.	Good, if you know in advance and information doesn't change.

LEAD TIME	Real time.	Two to six weeks; quicker delivery available, but at a premium.
RUNS	Can print variable length runs.	Most cost-effective method for long runs; can print up to 1,000 feet/minute.
GRAPHICS	Mostly limited to bar codes with few graphics.	Can print directly on product's packaging and combine graphics with bar code.
EXPERTISE	Need in-house production and quality control staffs for printing bar codes.	Some printers have up to ten years experience in all facets of bar coding.
EQUIPMENT	Wide range: under $1,000 to over $10,000.	No need for bar user to buy.
ORDER QUANTITIES	No restrictions.	Minimum ordering quantity generally enforced.
LABEL INVENTORY	None; print on demand.	Label inventories delivered to user.
PAPER INVENTORY	Need to store paper stock.	None; inventory at printers.
SCRAP	Little scrap, if label inventory kept low.	Left with remaining labels changes.

SELECTING A PRINTING SYSTEM

If the choice is to implement an internal printing system, the company should limit the use of the printers only to printing bar codes. Otherwise, the level of quality control which is needed to produce bar codes with acceptable first-pass read rates cannot be accomplished.

Do not select a printing system without also considering the choice of scanning equipment, label stock, adhesive and symbology. The choice of a printer is only one variable in the criteria used to select a bar coding system.

The question of which printer to choose really becomes a series of questions about what kind of label fits the application. The following five questions are key issues to address when selecting a printer:

1. What kind of information is needed on the label? Is it just a bar code? Or, a bar code and graphics?

2. How much information needs to be encoded? Most users think they need more information than is necessary. If bar codes are needed to satisfy a customer's requirements, then there may be a need to encode five or six different fields of information. But, for internal use where the bar coding system is linked to the company's computer system, there is no need to duplicate information which already resides in the data base.

3. Where will the label be used? Will it be affixed to computer chips, fixed assets, computerized reports or file folders?

4. In what kind of environment will the label be used? Will it be exposed to sunlight, chemicals, rough handling or extreme temperatures?

5. How long will the label have to last? How many times will it be scanned by a contact reader?

As for the printer itself, you need to consider several more areas:

1. Does the printer have sufficient print speed to handle the volume of labels you expect to print?

2. Will the printer's parts be able to withstand the expected volume of labels?

3. Will the feeding mechanism jam under constant use?

4. Does the printer have sufficient protection to safeguard against dirt, knocks, spills, etc. which are normal in warehouses or on shop floors?

5. Is the printer the most cost-efficient choice for your bar coding application?

6. How much space will the printing system take up?

7. Will you need special training in the printer's use? Will you need to hire personnel to run and maintain the system?

8. What are the costs of supplies, such as inks, ribbons, print heads, etc.?

9. What level of maintenance is required to ensure quality?

We believe it is important to benchmark the printer speed and other ratings for each manufacturer. In addition, it is very important to assess the business applications not only for the present , but for the future as well. Many companies forget about new processes, automation or new product requirements in their choice of printers and, indeed, all bar coding equipment. Bar coding cannot be treated as just a technical solution to a distribution or manufacturing site. It has to be treated as part of the total business solution.

SUPPLIER INVOLVEMENT

Suppliers, too, are part of the Total Business Concept. Many of our readers in the future will be asking suppliers to print bar code labels on the cartons, bottles and cases which they will ship to you. Supplier involvement in your program is important as is the involvement of the end customer. If both are involved during the process, many future problems will be avoided. A supplier left to make its own choice of equipment without considering your requirements may make the wrong choice. The quality theme of DO IT RIGHT THE FIRST TIME should prevail.

At this point, we are closer to knowing what type of bar coding system will fit our application. We have discussed symbologies and printing systems, but that still leaves scanners. In the next chapter, we will review the different types of scanners and how to select the one best suited to your specific needs or requirements.

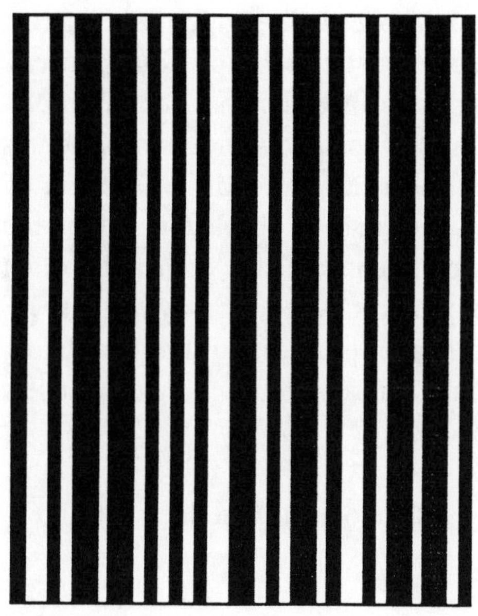

CHAPTER FOUR: Bar Code Readers

Another key element, along with the choice of a symbology and a printing device, is the choice of a reader. There are two main paths to take when the choice is made and these paths apply to the whole bar coding system as well. The traditional path is the MIS (Management Information Systems) approach. On this path, the user is not the driver in selecting the bar coding system which the MIS department is recommending, selecting and implementing. There is value in this approach, but it can end up as overkill since the emphasis is on integrating the company's data processing and not on integrating bar coding into company operations.

It is now possible to purchase bar code readers which have internal software that can prompt the operator through the reading process. Such a system, which needs little modification, can be implemented in one to three months. Compare this with the six months to a year which the MIS approach can take as it searches for an optimal solution, a solution which may be obsolete in that period of time. In addition, MIS departments in many companies often have a significant backlog of projects. We are not saying that MIS should not be part of the selection process, but the bar coding industry is moving far too rapidly through technological barriers to wait for a long amount of time.

The success of a bar coding system depends on three variables:

- Design of Label.
- Printing Device.
- Reader.

Many companies do not have a technical person who is well versed in all three variables. It is a full-time job keeping up with the latest developments in this growing industry. That is why it pays, in most cases, to use external assistance in selecting a pre-existing package from a vendor and to use their expertise to help implement the system. There is little sense in reinventing the wheel, although many companies do so because they feel that they are unique.

READER BASICS

Before we explain how a bar code reader works, let's clear up any confusion about the differences between a "reader" and a "scanner". A scanner is the device which produces a signal representing the bars and spaces of a bar code. A decoder then converts the signal so that a computer will understand the signal. The scanner and the decoder together make a bar code reader.

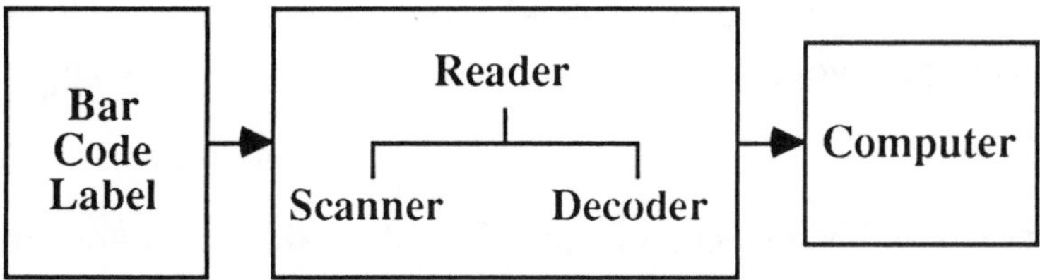

Major Components of Bar Code System

Every bar code reader has three parts — an illumination source, a photodector and a signal decoder or microprocessor. Since some form of light is used to read the bars and spaces in the code, it is important that the spot of light not be too small to pick up extraneous marks or voids and not be too large to miss narrow bars. Either case seriously impairs the efficiency of the reader and the quality level of the data.

Basically, two forms of light are used in bar coding — infrared and visible red. Infrared has the advantage of being able to read a number of different densities and to detect bar codes in unclean environments. Infrareds require carbon in the ink which makes it necessary for you to have a printing system with this capability.

OPTICAL THROW AND DEPTH OF FIELD

There are two other factors in selecting a bar code reader. The optical throw is the closest distance at which a scanner can read a bar code. In the case of contact scanners, this is almost zero. For some lasers, this distance can be up to seven feet. Optical throw is an important consideration which depends on the bar coding application. We wouldn't recommend using a scanner with an optical throw of six inches if the scanner was two feet away from the bar code. Conversely, if the best system for your application has an optical throw of six inches, you will have to consider redesigning conveyor or inventory systems to support the application.

Depth of field has the same meaning in bar coding as it does in photography. It is the distance in which a bar code is in focus or, to be more technical, the distance between the closest and farthest point at which a bar code can be read.

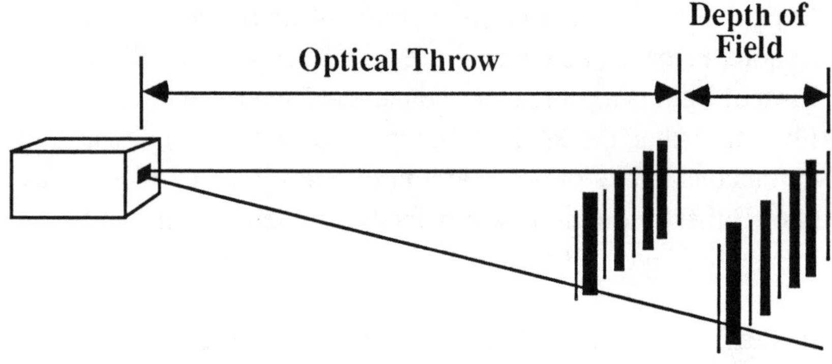

Depth of Field and Optical Throw

Like optical throws, depths of field vary for different scanners and have a direct impact on the implementation of a bar coding system for a particular application. Your choice of scanner must match the requirements of the symbology. Depth of field is also affected by the density at which you print.

METHODS OF DECODING

Once the bar code has been scanned, the data must be transferred from the microprocessor in the scanner to a computer system using some type of interface software. There are three types of bar code reader systems which read the signal and translate the data so that it can be understood by the computer. They are wedge readers, internal bar code boards and software shells.

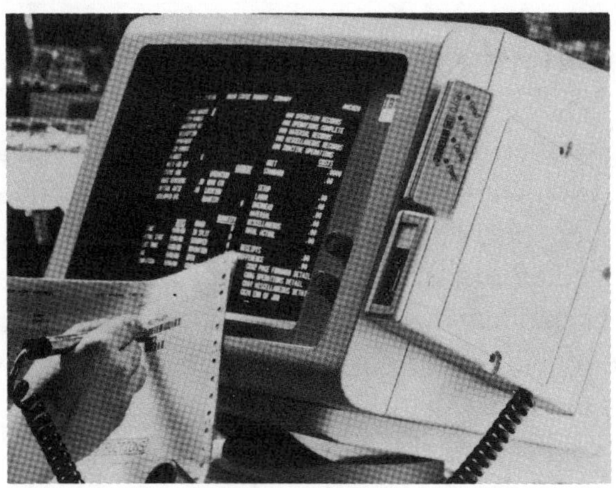

Wedge Reader

Photo Courtesy of Intermec

The wedge reader converts the bar code signal into a keyboard signal which the computer is already able to read. This interface system is the most widely used method of decoding and is implemented in the manner shown in the above diagram. Although wedge readers are relatively inexpensive by themselves ($250 - 800 each), you may need one at each point where a scanner is connected to a computer.

The internal bar code board plugs right into the computer. The board, like a wedge, converts bar code signals. However, there is at least one drawback. The computer must have an open architecture or a slot where the board can be plugged in.

The third method of decoding is the software shell which, in conjunction with the computer's operating system, simulates keyboard entry of bar code signals.

TYPES OF READING DEVICES

Bar coding reading devices can be divided into two categories — contact and non-contact. Contact readers require operators to use a wand or light pen which they then scan over the bar code by actually touching the label. Non-contact readers can either be hand-held or stationary (as they would be on a conveyor line). In either case, operators do not have to touch the label with the reader. The distance at which the label can be read varies according to the specific reader and its application.

Where to use contact or non-contact readers depends on what you are scanning. For example, if you are scanning a paper label on a hard, flat surface, then contacts are reliable and economical. If, however, the surface is curved (such as cans or bar stock) or rough, then non-contacts are preferred since the beam of emitted light "wraps" around the surface. The choice between the two also depends on how easily an operator can get to the label. If a reader is used in a receiving dock or similar environment where bar code labels are not in an identical, pre-arranged location that can be scanned easily by a stationary non-contact reader, then a portable contact reader is the best choice. Operators are then able to bring the reader to the package and not vice versa. Packages and other material can then be scanned without either bringing the packages to the reader or arranging them so that their labels are in the proper orientation. Contact readers are also the best choice for scanning bar code labels on paperwork whether in a receiving area, shop floor or office.

There are two exceptions to the use of a contact reader in the above situations. If received packages or material are shrink-wrapped, we would then recommend non-contact readers. Since the plastic covering does not give firm support to the attached bar code label, contact readers will not get a high percentage of first read rates. Non-contacts, which do not have to touch the label, get far better rates. The second exception occurs when you have labels of lesser quality. Non-contact readers read such labels at better read rates than contacts. We don't recommend this approach, however, because it treats a symptom and doesn't cure the disease. What this situation calls for is better labels, not a technological band-aid that covers up a mistake in design or implementation.

HAND HELD WANDS (LIGHT PENS)

A hand-held wand or light pen is approximately the size of a large marking pen. It is the most commonly used bar code reader because it is the least expensive and because there are a great variety of models available for use in any of a number of applications or environments. Light pens use either infrared or visible light depending on the conditions where they will be used (infrareds are generally better suited to unclean environments) or on the type of ink used in the printing process (infrareds can read only inks with a carbon content).

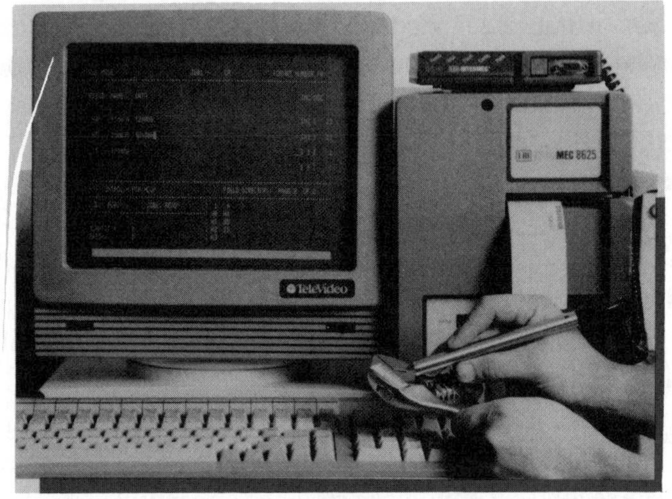

Hand Held Wand

Photo Courtesy of Intermec

The light pen is wanded across the bar code label and converts the bars and spaces into a signal which the computer system can interpret. Light pens have a first read rate of over 85% which indicates just how easy they are to use. Most operators can learn how to use a light pen properly in about ten minutes. With proper training, first read rates of 98% can be achieved.

Light pens also have the ability to be on-line with a computer system and those with memory can be programmed to prompt operators as they perform work. For example, a light pen can prompt an inventory picker to find a part number in a particular location. If the picker goes to the wrong location and wands the wrong bar code label, the light pen will inform the user that this is an incorrect read. Users can also have a menu or template upon which there are pre-assigned bar codes for operations which are frequently used. For example, a light pen user could simply wand the label representing the quantity of 100 whenever he picked 100 parts off the shelf. This action would take the place of keying in the number "100" manually and thus eliminate potential errors.

There are a large number of applications for light pens. We have listed some of the applications which have been successfully implemented by various clients:

- Receiving
- Shipping
- Production status reports
- Air freight shipments
- Warehouse/ storage location
- Work-in-process status
- Inventory control
- Labor reports
- Cycle counts
- Tool crib tracking

FIXED VS. PORTABLE READERS

Since portable contact readers are not tied to a computer terminal by a cord, they are more versatile than fixed, or stationary contact readers. There are applications, however, where fixed readers may be a better choice, for example, sorting envelopes, reading badges or identifying packages. Wherever the orientation and location of the bar code label is controlled, stationary readers are a distinct possibility.

In many applications, speed is of the essence when stationary readers are used to identify parts or boxes as they pass by on a conveyor. The bar code contains information which designates its final destination. The reader then transmits this information to a computerized system which opens or closes gates on the conveyor, thus routing boxes to the point where they are needed as well as updating the data base. In such a factory, stationary readers are something like a railroad worker who throws a switch to route railroad cars to their proper place in the yard. In this analogy, the computerized system acts as a dispatcher who gets information from the readers and then makes decisions. Of course, this analogy is not farfetched at all. One of the first applications for bar codes was to identify and track railroad cars.

In the application above, conveyors also orient boxes so that they are in the correct position for a good read. Position is a critical factor when using stationary readers. Boxes go by only once and a bad read can stall the whole operation. Equally critical is the printing quality of the label. Poor quality increases the chances for a bad read and a stalled operation. The last factor to consider when using stationary readers is the velocity at which boxes move by the reader. Obviously a line must be set up so that the movement of boxes matches the specifications of the reader.

As mentioned, portable readers offer flexibility and the ability to program the reader in order to prompt operators. Portable readers are also capable of storing up to a megabyte of alphanumeric characters in their memory. This information can then be downloaded into the company's computer system via modems or wedges. Some portable readers can be connected to the main computer in an on-line, real-time manner by means of radio frequency. For the most part, however, portable readers can do everything that a fixed reader can. The integrity of the stored data also matches that of fixed readers.

NON-CONTACT SCANNERS

The second major category of bar code reading devices is non-contact. As the name says, these scanners do not require the operator to make physical contact with the bar code label. As such, they are especially useful in applications where labels are difficult to reach or where the label is attached to a curved or pliable surface. Typically, non-contact scanners are shaped like a gun (if they are portable) which is then pointed at the label and the "trigger" squeezed to get a read. It is hard to establish a range of prices for non-contacts because new technology and applications have created a variety of models. In general, however, they are more expensive than contact readers. For those who are just starting to implement a bar code system, the steps that need to be taken to justify their cost will be covered in Chapter 7. Other features, besides cost, to consider when justifying the purchase of a non-contact scanner are first-read rate, depth of field and power consumption. As always, these features must be assessed in light of a specific application.

Non-contact scanners divide into two classes—fixed beam and

moving beam. Fixed-beam scanners are not the same as fixed or stationary scanners. Fixed scanners refer to the position of the reading equipment (i.e., fixed in one place) and not to the manner in which the light is projected in order to scan. Instead of a spot of light, fixed-beam scanners project an elongated beam of light which then scans a bar code as it passes.

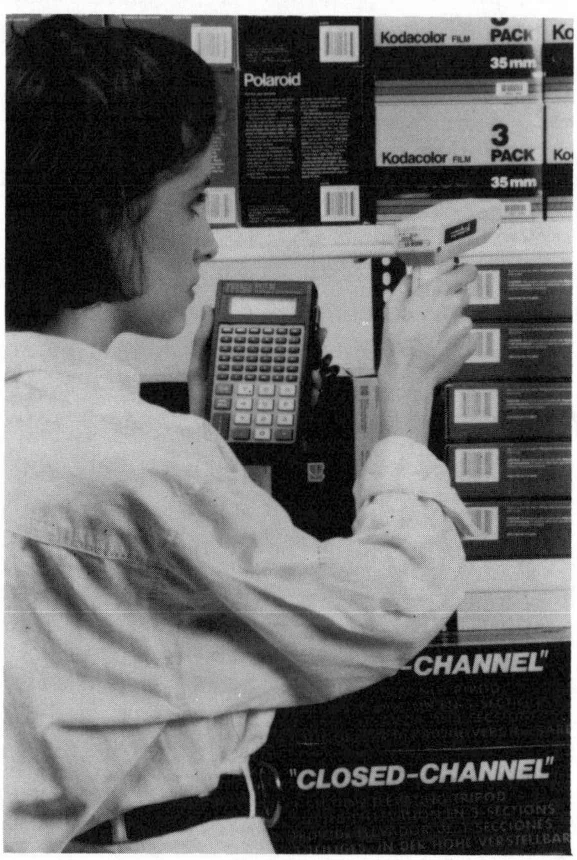

Non-Contact Scanner

Photo Courtesy of Symbol

This is to insure that printing defects will not cause a bad read since a larger area of the bars and spaces is covered. Because the beam is longer, however, the depth of field and optical throw of the reader is critical. Labels which are out of focus cannot be read.

Whereas a fixed beam scanner only gets one chance to read a bar code label, moving beam scanners are designed normally to scan a label between 28 and 60 times a second. Some models can even scan a label up to 1,200 times a second. This, of course, greatly increases the chances for a good read. A system of mirrors or an oscillating optical lens sweeps the beam across the label at a high rate of speed while moving the beam up and down the height of the bar code itself. Thus, each scan occurs on a slightly different plane which greatly diminishes the chances that a printing defect will cause a bad read.

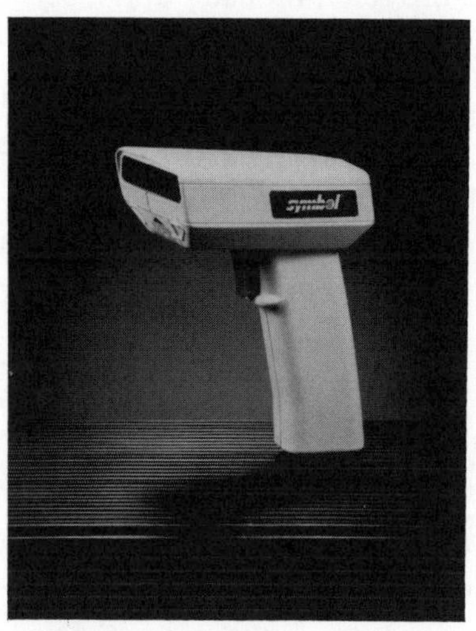

Moving Beam Scanner

Photo Courtesy of Symbol

The only drawback of moving beam scanners is that they can only read bar code labels about 7 to 8 inches in length for laser models and 2.5 inches for CCD (Charge Coupled Device) scanners. If your label is longer, the scanner will not be able to read it. Fixed beam scanners, on the other hand, can read longer labels since the beam is physically moved across the label by the action of an operator or a conveyor. Moving beam scanners, however, have the advantage of being easier for an operator to adapt to. Their high read rates do not frustrate operators and typically increase their productivity.

LED, CCD and LASER

There are three types of light sources used in non-contact scanners —LED (Light Emitting Diode), CCD, and laser. LEDs and CCDs are mostly used in the retail industry and lasers in manufacturing and warehousing applications. Principally, this is because of the greater versatility of lasers in reading a wide range of label densities. LEDs, which emit a visible light beam, also have a limited optical throw. The same can be said of CCDs, which scan labels electronically as do television cameras and facsimile machines. CCDs, in fact, can almost be labeled contact readers since they must be within approximately an inch of the label.

Lasers, on the other hand, emit light of only one wavelength. This concentrated beam allows for a greater depth of field and optical throw as well as the ability to read labels of different densities. The latter feature is particularly important in a company where different suppliers ship products with labels of varying densities. One laser scanner is capable of reading all of them whereas LEDs and CCDs can only read one particular density. In such a company, this would mean purchasing several scanners — one for high density labels, one for medium density and one for low density.

Laser scanners, including laser diodes which emit infrared light, are more expensive. But, as mentioned before, their ease of use can push productivity to higher levels which can more than offset their cost. Often, however, companies think they need a Lamborghini when a Toyota will do. Laser scanners represent the high-tech end of the bar coding industry. It could be better for you to get your feet wet with less technical equipment and, as you become more advanced, to enter into laser technology. Depending on your application, this may or may not be possible, but it is always better to start simple and then get more involved than the other way around.

OMNIDIRECTIONAL SCANNERS

Omnidirectional Scanner
Photo Courtesy of Symbol

Omnidirectional scanners are the ones we see in grocery stores. Cashiers move the package over a large scanning window in which a system of mirrors emit several laser beams which read the code. These beams intersect at several angles, thus allowing the package to be read at various orientations. This also enables omnidirectional scanners to read bar code labels on curved surfaces such as cans or through shrink wrapping such as meat and poultry. Mike Stanko, a ProTech director, states that these scanners are used by Philip Morris where wooden barrels of tobacco 10 feet in diameter can be read regardless of their orientation.

RADIO FREQUENCY

A radio frequency identification system (RFID) consists of an electronic tag or label which contains encoded information and a reader which activates the label with radio waves in order to read the information. Some systems are also capable of transmitting new information to the labels. Such labels are called Read/Write tags and, in many ways, are similar to floppy disks which, when inserted in a computer, can be read for information or be written upon to change information. Radio frequency is making possible a new era of "smart" labels which can be programmed to route material or record transactions whenever the label is used. In essence, the cables which link a computer to its terminals and peripheral equipment is simply replaced by radio frequency channels. The labels are then implanted with information which has been condensed into the electronic equivalent of bars and spaces.

At present, the field is relatively new and expensive, but technological advances are reducing prices and creating opportunities

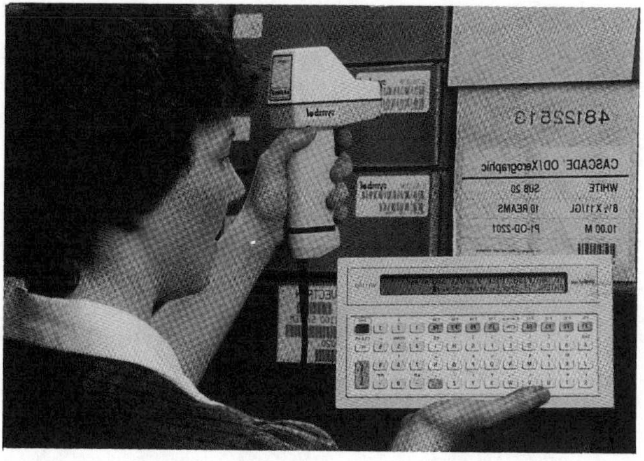

Radio Frequency System
Photo Courtesy of Symbol

for new applications. Although radio frequency is not recommended for beginning users, the field bears watching as does radio frequency data collection (RFDC) which is actually more common than RFID. RFDC actually reads the bar code label and then uses radio frequencies to transmit information to the computer. This is the ultimate in real-time application, but also the most expensive.

SELECTING A READER

There are an increasing number of bar code readers from which to choose as well as an increasing number of situations to which bar coding can be applied. Together, these two facts make the choice of a bar code reader a difficult one, but not impossible. Above all, you must remember to look at the whole picture, in other words, to take a systems approach which takes into account your choice of a symbology and a printer. With this mind-set, you can then ask yourself the following questions. They are typical of all applications of bar coding.

• *Do I want an automated or hand-held scanner? A portable or stationary scanner?*

This depends on how many reads you will make in an hour and whether it is easier to bring the item to the scanner or the scanner to the item.

• *How easy is it for an operator to get to the label?*

Hard to reach labels will require non-contact scanners. The distance between the scanner and label is a related factor here. Different models have different optical throws and depths of field. Determine the distance you will need in your application before making a choice.

• *What type of surface will the label be attached to?*

Hard, flat surfaces are more conducive to contact readers whereas curved or pliable surfaces are read better by non-contacts.

• *What environmental conditions will the label be subjected to?*

Heat and light will cause thermal labels to darken. Dirt, oil or grease will cause bad reads unless infrared scanners are used which can detect high-carbon inks below the smears and stains that occur on factory floors. Remember, too, that if you laminate or otherwise protect the label, this will affect your choice of scanner. In addition, ambient light can also curtail the effectiveness of fixed beam readers.

• *Will all labels in your application meet the specifications of the reader?*

In a closed system, in which no labels from outside suppliers intrude, you have control over label quality and density. However, in an open system, you will probably need a reader or readers capable of scanning varying densities and levels of quality.

• *What is a desirable first read rate?*

The answer to this question is directly related to the amount of training and education you will need to put into place for operators. As we have noted, moving beam scanners require less training, but cost more. What tradeoff is best for your application?

• *Do you need a programmable reader?*

This depends on the complexity of your application. Ask yourself how many repeatable operations there are and whether they can be encoded into a label which an operator then uses. As with the previous question, an increase in complexity means an increase in education and training. The costs and time may be well worth it, however, if the programmable reader means greater inventory accuracy, improved tracking or higher levels of productivity.

• *How much post-sales support does the bar code vendor supply?*

You will have questions once you begin to implement your system. Support is a cost factor which cannot be ignored.

THE SYSTEMS APPROACH

In the first three chapters, we introduced the major components required for a bar coding system. Now we need to discuss this network and how to achieve and maintain quality throughout the system.

Recently we came across an interesting situation which had to do with quality. Newell Window Furnishings, a client from Freeport, Illinois, had just finished conducting a supplier symposium on how to guarantee shipment of 100% good product. Patrick Jenkins, Newell's Purchasing Manager, found a note pad left behind by one of the participants. On the top sheet of paper in prominent letters was a question that he posed to his associate:

How do you get a supplier to ship 100% good product?

Below was the associate's answer:

You don't! You never will!

Pat Jenkins was so upset by this response that he sent off the following letter. Bear in mind as you read it that the same admonitions apply to the achievement of 100% quality in a bar coding system as well. It is the same negative attitude about quality that America needs to combat.

> Dear Supplier,
>
> Sometimes the most interesting comments are those which are unsolicited. I honestly thank you for the scratch pad notes left behind.
>
> I am disheartened to see a young, aggressive and talented newcomer buy off on the "good old boys" idea of "business as usual."
>
> How do you get suppliers to ship 100% good product? You wield a ***Huge Sword*** to cut and slash poor quality and overall wastefulness. The age old philosophy of "ship quantity and to hell with quality" must be challenged.
>
> I'm tired of our apathy toward business. Our generation must tip the scale, once again, back in favor of the U.S.
>
> What type of life (standard of living) are you going to leave your children? Think about it!! Each of us has an obligation to be the best.
>
> Warmest regards,
>
> *Patrick D. Jenkins*

In the next chapter, we will review the importance of quality as it applies to bar coding systems and applications. As Pat said, "Quality First!"

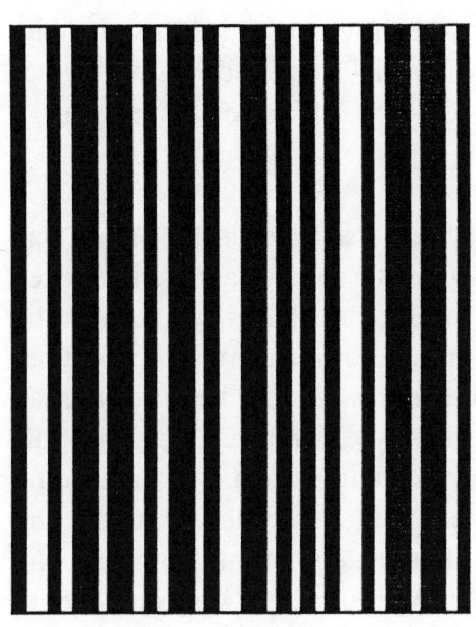

CHAPTER FIVE: The World of Bar Code Quality

It is possible to buy the best reader, the best label and the best printer and still have a bar coding system with less than desirable results. The missing ingredient is a systems approach. Quality is not assured by purchasing components which do not blend together into a symbiotic relationship. A perfect example of this comes from the world of sports. The Boston Celtics did not win 16 National Basketball Association championships with individual players who could out-shoot, out-rebound or out-defend their competition. Each Celtics players had a role to play, a role which complemented and enhanced the roles of their teammates. The Celtics blended together like the different parts of a symphony orchestra. Now teams like the Detroit Pistons and the Los Angeles Lakers have the blend required. We learn from others and then go forward.

The success of a bar coding system also depends upon more than purchased software and hardware. Bar coding has to be integrated into your company's long-term business plan if you expect the system to meet future needs. In addition, there must be a continuous education and training program in place. Otherwise, you can run into a problem with new employees who are not aware of the importance of quality in a bar coding system. We have come across several situations where programs which start and stop have had disastrous effects. Fortunately, at one company, the problem was seen early enough to be corrected. A pilot bar coding project was implemented at one plant of a company. The project leader then moved on to another plant to implement the system. The original project was taken over by a newly-hired operation manager. About a month later, the first pass read rates had dipped dramatically and nobody could figure out why. The company was using the same printers and scanners, but was still getting numerous bad reads. The outside consultant was called back and began checking every facet of the system. It turned out that the new operation manager, in an attempt to show how well he could cut costs, was purchasing cheaper label stock of inferior quality.

Consequently, the ink on the printer's ribbon was not absorbed properly. The labels were thus out of tolerance for the scanners and causing bad reads.

A few saved pennies in purchasing had caused a major disruption which could have been prevented by simply instructing the new operation manager about the absolute importance of quality in a bar coding system. In the chapter addressing implementation, we show you how to establish an education and training program and how to develop both short and long-term strategies.

THE WEB OF QUALITY

Every system needs a set of rules which delineates how the different components work as separate units and together as a whole. Because a bar coding system is complex and has numerous variables, it is difficult not to become bogged down in a level of detail which is of less importance to the project leader than a system-wide perspective. For this person, there is a need to sort all the factors affecting performance into manageable groups such as the ones below:

GROUP ONE:	**Application.**
GROUP TWO:	**Choice of Symbology.**
GROUP THREE:	**Environmental Factors.**
GROUP FOUR:	**Print Quality.**
GROUP FIVE:	**Reader Performance.**

Grouping factors not only makes it easier to understand and implement bar coding, but also easier to make choices. The first task of a project leader is to learn how these groups interact. You now know that a choice of a printer depends upon the character density of the chosen symbology. Print quality and symbology determine which reader will work best given the environment in which the reader must work.

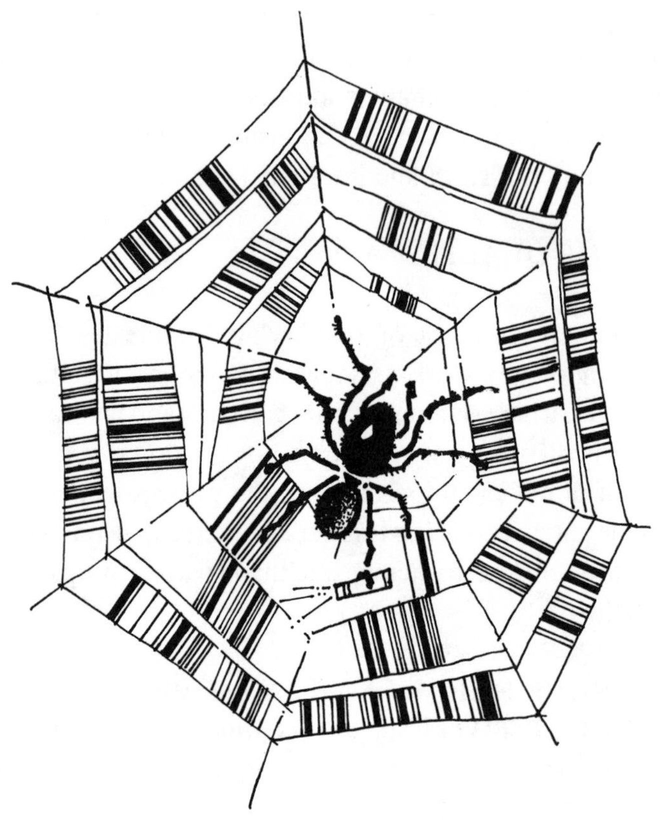

The Web of Quality

In our three previous books, **MADE IN AMERICA:** ***The Total Business Concept*****, JUST-IN-TIME PURCHASING:** ***In Pursuit of Excellence*** and **SUPPLIER CERTIFICATION:**

Achieving Excellence, we have used the image of a spider's web to explain the interconnected nature of a Total Business Concept (TBC). Touch a spider's web anywhere, we pointed out, and the effects ripple throughout the entire system of silken strands. This, too, is the phenomenon seen in a systems approach to bar coding. It should also be noted that a spider's web is an organic and integrated system. All parts of the web are necessary and sufficient. Spiders don't attach high-priced, high-tech machines or systems to their natural solution for catching dinner. The lesson for us is to let our bar coding systems grow naturally from the demands of the users and not to force solutions which will not work with the system as a whole.

The following descriptions of factors which affect bar code performance have varying effects on each of the groups above. Once you get down to this level of detail, it is impossible to say that one particular factor is primarily related to one group. For example, it would not be correct to say that the use of laminates is primarily an environmental factor since their purpose is to keep dirt off of labels. The use of a laminate will also directly affect the performance of the reader. This may mean that you will have to use higher quality ribbons when you print the label. Any time you change the quality of the printing, you must revisit your choice of symbology relative to the new printing specifications.

In short, there are no easy choices in bar coding. What you must do when presented with a choice is go back to the four groups and ask how the choice will affect each. In that way, you can think of yourself as the spider. Does the choice or change "fit" naturally into my web? Does it help or hinder my web from doing what it was designed to do?

FACTORS AFFECTING BAR CODE PERFORMANCE

BAR HEIGHT

For hand-held readers, bar height is at least one-quarter of an inch or 15 percent of the entire code's length, whichever is greater. The height of the bars in a label has a direct effect on readability, particularly the angle at which a label is read. Bar height also directly affects the physical act of scanning by an operator. The smaller the height, the more difficult it is to get a good read. In addition, bar height is a determining factor in print quality. Different printers have different capabilities. A printer that can print tall labels may not necessarily be able to print labels of lesser height and still retain high quality.

"X" DIMENSION

The "X" dimension is the width of the narrowest element of the bar code. Other elements of the code are multiples of the "X" dimension. Some symbologies have only two widths, narrow and wide, while others have up to 18. The resolution (see below) of the scanner determines how small the "X" dimension can be. Current technology allows for a value as low as 0.0075 mm or as high as 50 mm. With larger "X" dimensions, it is necessary to consider the aperture size (see below) of the scanner and the amount of space available for the label. Obviously, larger "X" dimensions take more room to print.

CHARACTER DENSITY

Density refers to the number of characters which can be encoded in a given unit of length and is vitally important to the eventual application of a bar code. Usually expressed as the number of characters per inch, density has two variables to consider. Compact codes, for instance, are usually more reliable, but require a high degree of print quality. There is little room for printing which is out of tolerance. Less compact codes have more flexible tolerances, but don't allow you to encode as much information on a label. Larger labels, of course, are easier to read by both human operators with scanners or by scanners which are fixed into position on a production line.

CONTINUOUS/DISCRETE

Bar code symbologies are either **continuous** or **discrete**. Continuous symbologies use the intercharacter gap as a character, whereas discrete symbologies do not.

FIRST PASS READ RATE

The first read rate is the ratio of the number of successful reads to the number of attempted reads. For example, 90 good reads out of 100 attempts yields a 90 percent first read rate. The first read rate does not only depend on the capabilities of bar code readers and their users. The print quality of the label and how that matches the capability of the reader also determines the readability of the code as do environmental factors such as the level of ambient light and the amount of dirt and oil which is present. A quality bar code system requires at least an 85 percent first read rate with a 99 percent read rate on the second try. Anything less is unacceptable.

SUBSTITUTION ERROR RATE

The substitution error rate is the ratio of the number of incorrect characters to the total number of entered characters. Because of the self-checking features of most symbologies, this factor, although important, causes few problems. The grandfather of symbologies, Code 39, does not normally require a check digit, whereas Code 93, 128 and UPC have a check digit built into their numbering schemes. Interleaved 2 of 5 may require a check digit, depending on the application and whether a fixed or variable field is being read.

RESOLUTION

Resolution is a measure of the size of the spot of light reflected back to the reader. In order to get successful reads or to print readable bar codes, the resolution of the bar code reader must match the resolution of the smallest module width. In other words, the aperture (see below) should match this module width. An aperture that is too small will pick up extraneous marks or voids. An aperture that is too large will miss narrow bars. Either case seriously impairs the efficiency of the reader. Resolution also affects print quality. Small resolutions are harder to hold to print tolerances, but they do allow for a greater density if that is needed. The industry uses the following general guidelines to define levels of resolution:

High Resolution	Less than 0.010 inches
Medium Resolution	Between 0.0101 and 0.030 inches
Low Resolution	Greater than 0.030 inches

APERTURE

The aperture is the measure of the size of the beam which reads the bar code. Since symbologies have different resolutions, aperture becomes a critical factor. Some readers are incapable of reading certain symbologies because their apertures do not match the resolutions of these bar codes. For contact readers, the reader is purchased for low, medium or high density. The same reader will not handle all three densities. Non-contact , LED (Light Emitting Diode) and CCD (Charge Coupled Device) readers also do not handle multiple densities, whereas lasers (both helium-neon and infrared) do. These are important considerations to review when analyzing user requirements.

TOLERANCE

Conformance to matching specifications (Symbology vs. Reader Resolution) is the essence of quality. Tolerances are influenced by the structural characteristics of the symbology. Obviously, a symbology with more degrees of latitude will make it less difficult for you to fall within the minimum and maximum tolerances for a printed symbol. This will mean that your readers and scanners must be capable of holding to the same printing tolerances. In other words, don't buy a dot matrix printer if your chosen symbology calls for strict tolerances that the printer cannot meet. If you keep the symbology, you will have to go to a printer with a higher resolution or to a commercial printer. If you keep the printer, you will have to change the symbology or perhaps use a moving beam reader which will forgive the poor resolution to some extent. It is far better, of course, to design a system in which all parts work together without resorting to jury-rigged solutions.

WIDE-TO-NARROW RATIO

The wide-to-narrow ratio is simply the ratio of a wide bar to a narrow bar in a symbology. Typical ratios are 2, 2.5, 3 and 3.5. The higher the ratio, the easier it is to read and print the code, depending on the reader and printer specifications. The trade-off for greater readability, however, is a loss of character density. Thus, small labels will generally have lower ratios in order to get the needed information into the allotted space and affect the quality of readability.

REFLECTIVITY

Reflectivity is defined as the amount of light reflected from the surface upon which the bar code is printed. It is important that you do not choose a paper, or other material, which interferes with the ability of a scanner to read the code. Whatever media you choose, it should reflect between 70 and 90% of the light from the illumination source back to the light detector. The higher the percentage, the better the media. White paper with a matte finish is preferred because it has a high reflectance and thus gives a better contrast between dark and light bars. Avoid situations where the media you have chosen does not match the capabilities of your readers. Also, you should be aware that a medium which is not opaque will allow light to be reflected from the surface upon which the label has been applied. This will result in background chatter which can disrupt signal interpretation. Finally, make sure that your system is capable of reading colored bar codes or bar codes printed on colored media. Infrared scanners, for example, cannot read all colors. They have problems reading blue/green combinations and cannot read thermal papers.

PRINT CONTRAST

Since readers operate by noting the difference in reflected light between the bars and spaces of a bar code, print contrast must be at a maximum. That means the ratio of the difference in reflected light, or Print Contrast Signal (PCS), should be greater than 70%. The quality of the printer, the reflectivity of the media as well as the properties of the ink and ribbon, if used, are all important considerations which directly impact print contrast. Also remember that environmental factors, such as heat, sunlight or dirt, have a bearing on the level of print contrast. It would be unwise to forget the conditions to which your labels will be subjected. Once again, the best equipment does not spell success if environmental factors are not included.

The formula for calculating the PCS is:

$$\mathbf{PCS} = \frac{\mathbf{RS - RB}}{\mathbf{RS}}$$

RS = Space Reflectance
RB = Bar Reflectance

The values for Space Reflectance and Bar Reflectance can be found with the use of an analyzer which we will discuss later in this chapter. It is simply a device which measures the various specifications of a bar code label. The PCS value should be as close to 1.0 as possible. Below 0.7, the PCS will cause problems in a bar code system.

OPTICAL THROW

The optical throw is the closest distance at which a scanner can read a bar code. Optical throw depends on your application of bar coding. We wouldn't recommend using a scanner with an optical throw of six inches if the scanner was always going to be two feet away from the bar code. Conversely, if the best system for your application has an optical throw of six inches, redesigning a conveyor or inventory system must be considered.

DEPTH OF FIELD

Depth of field has the same meaning in bar coding as it does in photography. It is the distance in which a bar code is in focus or, to be more technical, the distance between the closest and farthest point at which a bar code can be read. Laser readers have a depth of field which approaches 80% of the optical throw. This means that a laser reader with an optical throw of five feet is in focus anywhere from one foot to the maximum distance. This is particularly important if the application demands the ability to scan from different distances as in applications like warehouse picking.

SCANNING SPEED

As noted in the previous chapter, moving beam scanners are able to scan a code up to 1,500 times a second, although 30-60 times is more common. Even at the lower speed, this means that one pull of the reader's trigger gives you 30 scans which greatly increases the probability of a good read. In the case of contact or fixed beam readers, they should allow operators to scan across the label at variable rates. Since people work at different speeds, a reader which could only get a good read at a constant speed would be of little use.

WAVELENGTH

The wavelength of light emitted by the illumination source in a bar code reader can be in either red-visible or infrared ranges. It can also be composed of more than one wavelength or concentrated into one such as in laser readers. Wavelength can play a role in applications in which security is important. Then, for example, it is possible to print a black on black label in which the bar code itself is printed with carbon-based ink. This ink can be read by an infrared scanner and still allow the label to remain hidden. Wavelength will principally be a factor of your application of bar coding. Infrared, for example, is used in unclean environments or where confidential information is bar coded.

BAR CODE MEDIA

Bar code media refers to the paper or other material upon which the label is printed. There are two areas to which you must pay particular attention in order to obtain high first read rates:

1. **Print contrast and Reflectivity** — The media should reflect light at 70-90% efficiency. The way the light is reflected is important as well. That is why matte finishes are preferred over glossy finishes.

2. **Durability** — If the label will be scanned more than 50 times, some type of laminate or coating is necessary to protect the label. In harsher environments, metal, polyester or other media are necessary.

PRINT QUALITY

How important is print quality? To the main character in the movie ***Brazil*** by Terry Gilliam of Monty Python fame, it means everything. All of the sometimes amusing, but largely terrifying things that happen to him in the movie as he is hounded by a police state are the result of a printing error. The opening scene of the movie shows a computer printer spouting out reams of paper. There is a man in the room as well who is being bothered by a buzzing fly. He eventually kills the insect with a fly swatter. The dead fly falls into the printer causing it to misprint one letter in our hero's name. Our innocent functionary in one of the government's bureaucracies is mistaken for an enemy of the state. All because a fly fell into the printer, our hero undergoes a Kafkaesque nightmare.

Quality of Print

Bar code print quality does not have to be a nightmare, if certain areas are paid attention to:

1. **Bar width** — Can the printer print characters with the correct density and still maintain tolerances for width and resolution?

2. **Paper Thickness** — Will the thickness of the paper affect the tension at which the paper is held in the printer? Improper tension causes "phasing." Poor phasing results in an uneven bar edge which dramatically affects reader performance.

3. **Maintenance** — The minimum requirement for doing a periodic check of all your printing equipment is six months.

RIBBON FACTORS

The principal rule to remember with ribbons is that the ribbon you use in the office will probably not meet the specifications or requirements of the bar coding environment. If you are thinking of doubling up on your ribbon use, test the ribbon on a bar code printer before employing it in the system. In addition, there are several other factors which must be taken into account:

1. **Ink Spread** — New ribbons tend to print wider bars and older ribbons produce smaller bars. This is a critical dimension to a bar code reader. Care must be taken that the ink from the ribbon does not spread or shrink beyond tolerances.

2. **Wetness**—Ribbons from different manufacturers vary in the amount of ink on them. Sometimes, the amount of ink even varies from lot to lot. You must be careful that a variation does not compromise the print quality. Once again, you should test ribbons if you are buying them from a new supplier.

3. **Ribbon Life**— It is very important that you know how long the ribbon will continue to print labels which have acceptable read rates. As noted, older ribbons print less distinct characters which will impair the reader's performance.

4. **Drying Speed** — Inks which dry quickly are preferred over slow-drying inks so as to avoid smearing or smudging. Remember: if a human can read a smudged label, it does not necessarily mean a bar code reader can. The human eye is much more forgiving than a bar coding system.

PAPER FACTORS

The paper chosen for a bar code system must conform to certain requirements as well. Paper should be free of flaws which may cause bars to be wider or narrower than desired. For that reason, recycled paper is not recommended for bar code applications. The paper should also be free of excessive shrinkage when ink is applied. Even a small amount of shrinkage can distort a bar to the extent that it is not readable. Thus, the paper should be absorbent, that is, allow the ink to sink into the paper and dry quickly. Finally, paper should be in colors which do not reduce the Print Contrast Signal. Only sophisticated users should attempt to use colored paper.

PACKAGING FACTORS

Although it sounds obvious, great care must be taken to ensure that the label is put on the package smoothly whether it is done by hand or with an applicator. Wrinkles or ripples in the paper will cause light to be reflected at odd angles which the reader will not be able to interpret accurately.

Packaging Factors

As noted before, the placement of the label on the package is important as well. Since boxes have six sides, random placement will only generate a probability of a one in six proper orientation. It is far better to select a side and a position on that side in order to allow the bar code system to do what it does best — read information accurately and quickly.

LABEL ENVIRONMENT FACTORS

We have discussed these factors at length before. Dirt, oil and grease will impair the performance of the bar code reader. Rain can wrinkle labels or cause ink to run. Sunlight and heat will cause some labels to fade or otherwise discolor. Don't overlook these factors in a bar coding application. It may be necessary for you either to change your system or change where labeled material is stored.

Environmental Factors

LAMINATES

In many ways, the specifications which apply to paper also apply to laminates. Laminates should not interfere with the scanning ability of the bar code reader. They should not be so thick as to obscure the printing below or so thin as to allow environmental factors to damage the label. Labels can be laminated up to 10 mils without a problem. Above that level, however, it is advisable to test the reader and the lamination in the environment in which the label will be used. As with paper, dull or matte finishes are preferred over shiny or gloss finishes.

ADHESIVES

Adhesives vary with each application. Some require labels to be permanently affixed to an item, such as a piece of capital equipment. Other labels need to stay affixed for awhile before they are removed. Such an application would be found in airline baggage terminals. Labels for New York destinations need to be removed when baggage changes planes in Chicago, for example. Adhesives also must be able to withstand the environmental conditions to which they will be subjected. For example, in one application we know, a university library put bar code labels on their books. A few months later, the humidity in the library caused the labels to fall off.

MEASURING PERFORMANCE — VERIFIERS AND ANALYZERS

As seen in the descriptions of performance factors above, there are a number of variables to consider in bar code quality, just as there are in any manufacturing process. In this respect, the production of bar code labels and their maintenance must be treated with the same kinds of controls that would be placed on a production process. This means that we do not inspect for quality after the label is printed; we must build quality into the bar code system. Readers and printers should be on a regular maintenance schedule. Brands of paper stock and ribbons should not be changed until it is proven that they can perform at acceptable levels. Still, even with the system controls, no system is infallible. A blob of ink in the wrong place can create havoc just as it did for the poor soul in the movie ***Brazil***. The worst bar code nightmare is not a label that cannot be read because it is poorly printed or damaged, but a label which reads fine and gives incorrect information. This affects everything from inventory accountability to costing. The diagram below shows such a possibility.

Character "6" with a Printing Void

Character "6" Transposed into a "4"
by Two Printing Defects

That is why verifiers, instruments which scan a label and tell the operator if it is a good or bad read, are not usually sufficient to maintain quality. A good read, as seen above, could produce the wrong information. What is needed is an instrument which will tell the operator why a given label is causing a bad read — wet ribbons, incorrect tension, improper ink, etc. Such an instrument is an analyzer. It should be used as an auditing tool to prevent unknown changes from entering into the bar code system.

Whether you print labels in-house or receive them from an outside printer, periodic samples should be taken and tested with an analyzer. Analyzers should check such areas as:

1. **Quiet Zones** — Are the areas in front and in back of the bar code free of printing defects?

2. **Voids and Blobs** — Is the system within tolerance?

3. **Bar Edge Roughness** — Is the edge sufficiently clear to be within dimensional specifications?

4. **Print Contrast Signal** — Is there sufficient contrast between the bar and the media it is printed upon?

5. **Bar/Space Widths** — Are these widths within tolerances?

Using algorithms, analyzers measure all the dimensions and properties of a bar code label to make sure that they will not only produce an acceptable first pass read rate, but that they will continue to produce repeatable reads. After all, one good read per label is hardly good enough. Also not good enough is sending a product to a customer with an unreadable label. Customers attempting to read the bad label will blame the poor quality on the product, not the label. This is a situation which can be avoided if attention is paid to the system-wide aspects of bar code quality.

Staying within the tolerances of a symbology's specifications will prevent almost all problems. That is why these standards have been developed. A Code 39 reader is manufactured, for example, to look for the specifications below whether that reader is in Alaska or Florida, on a receiving dock or on an assembly line. If the implementor of a bar code system does his or her homework and does not take shortcuts, quality will be the result.

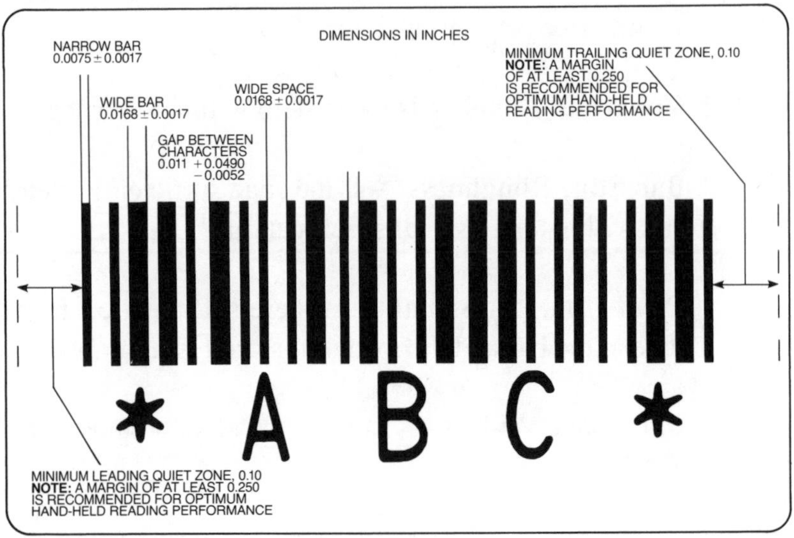

Printing Specifications for Code 39

LABEL QUALITY

A bar code system is only as good as the labels you are printing and reading. Previously, we discussed the advantages and disadvantages of printing labels in-house or having them printed by a commercial printer. Whatever choice is made, the quality of the label is of paramount importance. Based on his implementation programs, Wayne Douchkoff, a noted and frequent lecturer for numerous universities recently stated that at least 90% of the problems with bar coding result from poorly printed or maintained labels. Labels are subject to a number of factors which diminish their effectiveness. Improper adhesives cause labels to peel off as we saw in the library example above. Harsh or unclean environments cause labels to fade, discolor or even to deteriorate. Mr. Douchkoff also said that controls ***must*** be in place to consistently produce a label which can be accurately read by the bar code reader and effectively used by the whole system. Keep this in mind: a bar code label contains one of a company's most valuable resources—information. Loss of information or inaccurate manipulation of information can be highly detrimental to a company's operations.

Mr. Douchkoff emphasizes that this level of quality, as reflected in first pass read rates, must be much higher than we are used to accepting. For instance, a 97% read rate is not adequate, although many companies would be happy to achieve that level in other aspects of their company. In an environment where there are, for example, 10 different work stations that a bar-coded item must pass through, a 97% read rate at each translates into a 74% rate for the total system. This is far from adequate. Bar code print quality must achieve levels of 99.99% to be effective, but this is not impossible. The following checklist for label design and production will help bar code users achieve that level.

Adequate	Not Adequate	
________	__________	QUIET ZONE — Adequate space needed before and after the bar code in order to clear the reader for new information.

Adequate	Not Adequate	
______	________	**LABEL SIZE** — Label must be large enough for an operator to scan without difficulty and for human readable characters to be visible if necessary.
______	________	**BAR HEIGHT** — Bar height must also be sufficiently large for ease of scanning.
______	________	**ENVIRONMENT** — Label must be able to withstand temperatures, chemicals, abrasion, dirt, lighting found in area of application.
______	________	**ADHESIVES** — Label adhesive must be able to withstand environmental factors above.
______	________	**TYPE OF SCANNING** — Contact or non-contact.
______	________	**SHELF LIFE** — How long must the label last?
______	________	**GRAPHICS** — Is your printer capable of producing the graphics on your label as well as the bar code? Will the graphics interfere with the functioning of the reader?
______	________	**PRINTER REQUIREMENTS** Number of labels needed: Average Daily, Peak and Off-peak Requirement.

TYPICAL QUALITY PROBLEMS

The following chart is not meant to be inclusive. It would be impossible to predict every problem since each bar coding application has its own particular set of problems which must be overcome. The problems presented here, however, are typical and can cause havoc with the whole system.

PROBLEM	CAUSE	SOLUTION
Reflectivity	Mismatched media or lamination	Choose media or lamination which allows for maximum print contrast; choose reader capable of distinguishing between media and bar code.
Contrast	Inadequate Print Contrast Signal	Check media; check ribbon ink; check printer capabilities.
Print flaws	Ink spread	Check absorption rate of paper; check ribbon wetness; check hammer pressure.
	Ink shrinkage	Check ribbon wear; check hammer pressure.
	Ink voids or blobs	Check print head; check paper for foreign materials; check for defective ribbon.
	Ink smearing	Check paper quality; check ribbon wetness.
	Non-uniform inking	Check print head; check ribbon.
Poor read rates (dot matrix)	Wide/narrow module ratio	Use 3 to 1 module ratio
Label durability	Excessive wear or deterioration.	Check environmental factors; determine number of scans over life of label.
Environment	Paper discoloration	Check heat and sunlight levels.
Poor system	Inadequate maintenance	Develop a periodic maintenance performance schedule for all components of the bar code system.

Remember that quality is not the responsibility of a Quality Control or a Quality Assurance department. Quality is everybody's responsibility. It begins at the operator level. Operators must be responsible for the quality of the system they are using and have the authority to solve quality problems. This concept of quality will be discussed in more detail in Chapter 8 which deals with the implementation of a bar code system. Like any manufacturing process, quality should not be inspected for; ***it should be built into the system***.

Now that the different components of a bar code system have been explained and the procedures for achieving quality have been established, let's look at the different applications for which a bar coding system can be used.

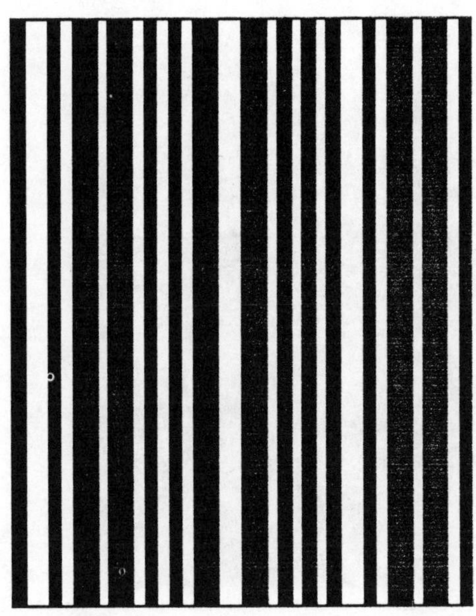

CHAPTER SIX: Business Applications

All applications of bar coding are based on what this technology does best: Providing fast, accurate and reliable data to all levels of a company. If a part, operation or system involves movement, counting or tracking (and what business operation doesn't?), then a bar coding application can be developed. That covers a lot of territory. In fact, bar coding is still young enough as an industry that all of its potential territory has not been explored or charted. Thus, bar coding presents a great opportunity for innovative people who are able to look beyond present-day applications. Such an individual will not see bar coding as a surgical operation which grafts a solution onto the body of the company. Rather, he or she will see bar coding as the very veins and arteries which keep the body of the company alive.

Avis Person Using Bar Coding for Car Rental Returns

Ultimately, bar coding is about information. As companies begin to automate and to use Just-In-Time (JIT), Total Quality Control (TQC) and Computer Integrated Manufacturing (CIM) in the management of their operations, then bar coding will become the veins and arteries which carry that information. These forward-looking companies will use bar coding to put information needed to make decisions into the hands of the operator as well as the Chief Executive Officer. No longer will a company be able to function as autonomous departments which have control over their own realms of information. Responsibility, authority and accountability will be fostered by the application of bar coding as it interconnects the various independent areas of a company into one mutually dependent whole.

In companies where bar coding has knitted the parts together with information, a long list of new possibilities will result. The newly available information will allow companies to use the following:

1. **"WHAT IF..." SIMULATION.**
2. **MODULAR SCHEDULING.**
3. **DETAIL CONTROL OF OPERATIONS.**
4. **RAPID DATA RETRIEVAL AND UPDATE.**
5. **RAPID AND CURRENT DOCUMENT PREPARATION.**
6. **ELECTRONIC INSTRUCTION SYSTEMS AT WORK STATIONS.**
7. **ELECTRONIC READING AND COUNTING.**
8. **JOB DISPATCHING AND AUTOMATED CONTROL FROM SAME COMPUTER.**
9. **LOADING AND SCHEDULING QUEUES.**
10. **TRACKING OF ENGINEERING DRAWINGS.**
11. **PROPERTY MANAGEMENT.**
12. **TIME AND ATTENDANCE.**
13. **COORDINATION OF MATERIAL, LABOR, MACHINERY AND TOOLS.**
14. **ELECTRONIC DATA INTERCHANGE (EDI).**

Of course, each of these applications and ones in the future will require the integration of hardware, software and human imagination. In the past, the vast majority of bar code applications were the work of a dedicated person or team which developed the necessary equipment and programs. These people often worked in-house and their solution was unique to the company in which they worked. Now, however, bar coding has grown to the point where "off-the-shelf" software is available, relatively inexpensive and reliable. For under $1,000, it is now possible to buy a data management program which prints bar code labels as well as collects and manages data. This is helpful, but it should be remembered as we discuss various applications of bar coding that there is no substitute for human imagination and creativity or a Total Business Concept (TBC).

PRESENT APPLICATIONS IN INDUSTRIES

The following industries use bar coding extensively today. Many of the applications within the industry have become standardized, that is, software packages already exist. For the company new to bar coding, this is a decided advantage. It means that your company may not need to re-invent the wheel and that you will be able to learn from those who have already developed the application you are interested in. Our advice is that you attend seminars and establish internal education and training programs.

INDUSTRIES USING BAR CODING

Hospitals
Libraries
Manufacturing
Government/Military
Retail
Automotive
Distribution

A few of the fundamental applications for which bar coding is being used in these industries are:

1. **Counting.**
2. **Data collection.**
3. **Information call-up.**
4. **Signalling to conveyor director gates.**
5. **Send-ahead orders and instructions.**
6. **Selection and control of machine instructions.**
7. **Instruction and control of production line robots.**
8. **Instruction and control of CNC (Computerized Numeric Control) equipment.**

Still another indication of the many applications of bar coding in these industries are the different items to which labels are applied. This is a partial list:

Packages
Trays or bins
Parts or assemblies
Job cards
Time cards
Bills of material
Picking lists
Payroll checks
Invoices
Badges
Assemblies
Tools
Law cases
Tags
Travelers
Labor tickets
Receivers
Bin identification cards
Routings
Inspection reports
Accounts payable checks
Purchase orders
Components
Finished goods
File folders
Kanban cards

As can readily be seen, this is a varied list which includes operations or procedures common to almost all business. Although companies are unique, even within an industry, the majority of a company's tasks are basically the same as those of any other company. Again, this is where bar coding shines. It is flexible enough to be adapted to any company's particular needs, but standard enough for its applications to be transferred from one company to another.

A recent survey by Frost & Sullivan asked bar code users just what are those applications. The following profile shows which applications are most common as well as some indication of the range of uses:

APPLICATION	PERCENT
Inventory management and control	47%
Work-In-Process monitoring and control	45%
Shipping	41%
Production counting	32%
Data entry	30%
Process control	24%
Automated warehousing	20%
Receiving	19%
Document processing	17%
Order processing	13%
Sortation	11%
Analytic systems and testing	5%
Automatic billing	3%

Percentages add up to more than 100 because many companies have more than one application.

So far, only the most general categories of applications have been discussed, categories which include manufacturing process monitoring, distribution of products, assembly verification, production status reporting, generation of shipping documentation, document control, visitor control, configuration labels and receiving from suppliers. The territory of bar coding applications has been defined, but not yet charted. To see what's in store, let's look now at some of the procedures, processes and data which bar coding can identify, track or count in two of these general categories.

The first category is the area of company procedures and processes. Bar coding can be used to accomplish the following:

Collect data.
Code documents.
Record time.
Count.
Identify.
Verify.
Index.
Instruct robots and equipment.
Control conveyors.
Perform automated stacking.

The second category is the work center. Here, bar coding can be used to:

Schedule.
Appropriate levels of Bill of Material.
Route Bills of Material.

Report area stock status.
Total authorized capacities.
Indicate labor availability by capacity.
Report requirements per schedule.
Indicate energy restraints.
Activate machine loads per schedule.
Process labor tickets.
Make material requisitions.

This is just a hint of what bar coding can do. Later in this chapter, we will discuss in more detail how some companies have taken their needs and translated them into bar coding applications.

APPLICATIONS AND MATERIAL FLOW

The flow of information which bar coding facilitates has greatly affected the material flow cycle within manufacturing companies, both in the JIT and traditional environments. Since our first book, **MADE IN AMERICA**, we have seen an increase in interest for JIT solutions using bar coding. Managing the flow of information in a JIT environment has become a major application of bar coding, great enough to deserve a discussion of its own. Bar coding seems to have been made to meet the needs of this cycle, since its speed, accuracy and reliability are essential to the maintenance of up-to-date records of inventory and production. Now, every time a procedure has taken place or a requisition made, the bar code system updates the company's database immediately. When it comes to making decisions, what more could a manager, executive or production personnel ask for? Finally, there is a solution which requires less paperwork.

Material first comes into Receiving as shown in the diagram on page 143. Here, boxes and invoices can be wanded to put information about the received lot into the computer system. All this information will be accessible throughout the cycle by scanning the bar code label attached to the part or the material. If there is an inspection operation in the receiving area, then bar codes can be used to register whether the material was good, rejected or returned to the suppliers.

Once the material has been received, it is then sent on to a storeroom. Parts, boxes, trays or bins of the material are wanded again to register their arrival and then to identify where the material will be stored. The part number, supplier, date of receipt and lot number are all that needs to be encoded on the label in order for the computer system to bring up the material's "history." Bar coding, in this sense, is like a bloodhound which searches for the trails of "scent" left by the material in its journey through the company.

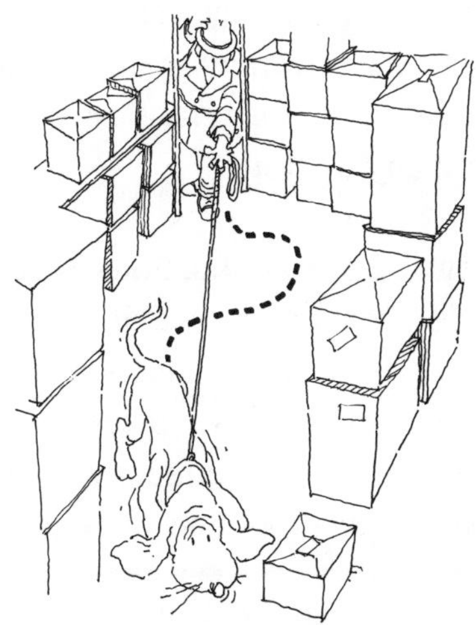

Tracking the Bar Code Trail

While in the storeroom, bar codes are also useful for doing cycle counts and physical inventory.

When the material is issued from the storeroom to the floor, bar codes are wanded to record this movement. As the material winds its way through Work-In-Process, bar code labels make sure that the right material has arrived at the right place at the right time. Here we can begin to see the usefulness of bar coding in a Just-In-Time environment.

The production phase of the cycle finished, material is now packaged in containers which bear bar code labels. Now the system has the added information of when the finished goods were made, what lot they are from, where the raw material or subassemblies came from and so on. All at the touch of a wand scanning across a label. In the final operation, the boxes are shipped from the facility to another factory, a distribution center or perhaps a retail store. Each produced part (as well as the carton) will bear a bar code label containing information important to the customer. Indeed, in a certain way, the material flow cycle begins again at the customer's company or store.

From this overview of the applications of bar coding in the material flow cycle, one can see that a detailed strategy is necessary. This overview simultaneously indicates the complexity of a bar coding system and its simple, overriding purpose. No matter how sophisticated the bar code system is in any environment, its purpose is always the same — providing fast, accurate and reliable information.

Let's turn now to a discussion of what bar coding can do and how

RECEIVING

(see P.142)

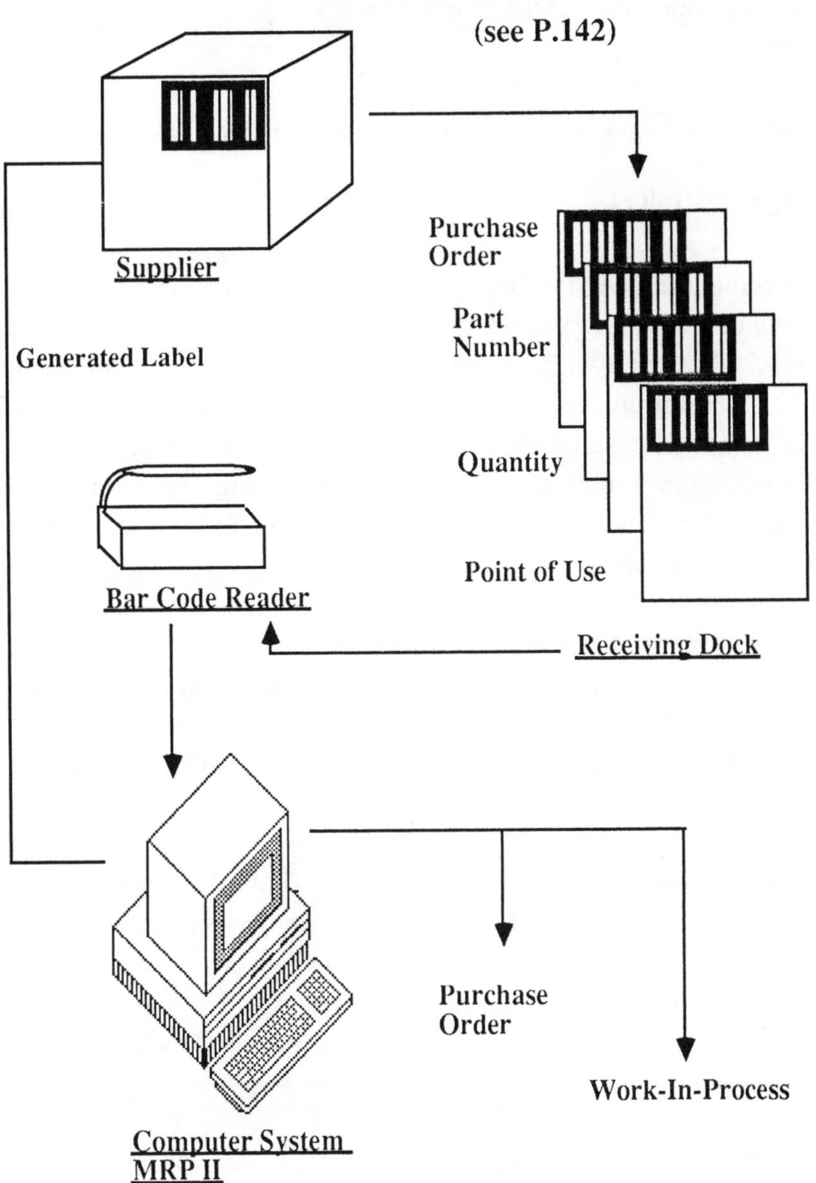

it has been implemented in specific applications. The selected areas divide into two major categories — operations and administration.

BAR CODING APPLICATIONS IN OPERATIONS

RECEIVING

Whether the receiving dock gets shipments with bar codes already applied by suppliers or whether the receiver must print and apply labels for their own internal use, the applications of bar coding in the receiving area are the same. Labels identify the item, purchase order number, supplier, lot number, date of delivery, etc. This information is then used to create a receiving and purchasing record which will be part of the material's history throughout its cycle. This ensures lot traceability.

For those suppliers who ship products with bar code labels, material often comes with a label attached to the shipping invoice as well. This label can then be scanned allowing the computer to compare the information on the invoice with the information contained in the original purchase order and, thus, help accounts payable to reduce paperwork. In fact, with the increased and frequent deliveries required by Just-In-Time, bar coding can greatly aid in reducing all paperwork. Many customers are now supplying bar code labels to their suppliers when a purchase order is placed. When such a partnership exists with a supplier, it is far easier to get the cooperation needed to agree on bar code symbologies and equipment.

Supplier Certification, as discussed in our book on the subject, makes it possible for receiving personnel to be aware of the status of any purchase order. With a bar code system, they will be alerted to any potential problems long before the material has been sent to the warehouse or the production line. Supplier cooperation has reached a point in the Far East where some suppliers wand their own products when they are delivered to the customer. This eliminates the need for a large receiving department at the customer's company. In Japan, we witnessed a plant receiving product with labels which indicated where the material would be processed. The bar code labels directed the boxes of parts to the proper operator in the plant.

The use of bar coding in receiving can also alert personnel to priority items. The system will have already tagged these items in its database. Thus, when a receiving employee wands the needed item, he will be prompted by the system to direct the material to where it is urgently needed.

The use of bar code labels in receiving can also pave the way for its eventual use in putaway operations and in location control. The system, for example, already knows where received material should be stored or where it should be sent on the factory floor. Perhaps most helpful is the fact that during all of the operations described here, a bar coding system records every transfer of material. The result is an inventory count which is not only accurate, but up-to-date. No more guesses or long searches for material that should be there, but isn't.

One large mail-order company turned to bar coding in order to integrate automatic identification, material handling control, distribution processing and database management into one receiving system. It created an internal system which does not rely on the supplier's label. This is because not all of their suppliers use bar coding. When a scheduled shipment arrives, a receiving room employee creates a shipment record using the paper invoices from the supplier. From this information, he then prints a bar coded identification label to be applied to each case as it is unloaded from the truck. Once inside the receiving area, the label is scanned for each case and the system prompts the operator to enter the stock number and quantity of the contents in the case.

Cases containing only one stock number are immediately routed to a storage area where the location is noted and then entered into the system using the case's unique bar code label. Cases containing more than one stock number are routed to a sortation area where individual labels are applied to the contents or to boxes within the case. When the cases or boxes leave the receiving areas, operators once again scan the attached labels. The information they receive back from the system tells them where to send the items and whether the contents and quantities agree with both receiving invoices and purchase orders.

INSPECTION/TESTING

Our business philosophy seeks to eliminate inspection whenever and wherever possible. But inspection is still part of the typical American company's cycle and so we cannot ignore it. Inspection of material usually occurs when the product arrives at the receiving dock. There, the bar code label is read so that inspection data can be entered for each attribute that is checked. Then, parts that pass inspection are delivered to storage or work-in-process. Defective parts are sent back to the supplier for replacement. Bar coding allows inspectors to accumulate data which can then be sent to suppliers for corrective action.

At an aerospace company, where quality is of paramount importance, material at the receiving dock is labeled with a bar code which identifies the part's priority in the inspection schedule and where it is to be stored while waiting inspection. When the product is ready to be inspected, an operator can wand a command on a template. This will call up the part number to see where it is located. At the same time, the system keeps track of how many parts are left to be inspected as well as how many have been inspected. In the event of a bad part, this company knows immediately where the part came from and when it was delivered. Appropriate measures can then be taken with each supplier.

At Apple Computer's Macintosh plant, the objective was to use bar code labels to tell a tester what test was required during the manufacturing process. The goal was to eliminate inspection and implement testing as a long-range objective. In addition, bar coding fit in with the plant's goal of paperless processing.

A pharmaceutical company uses bar coding to inspect the product labels which it applies to the containers and to check to see whether the label matches what is being put inside. Bar codes have already been used to ascertain what medicines are being placed in the containers. A scanner then reads the bar code on the product label to make sure that the two match. Obviously, this is of importance to a company which must identify and verify over 50,000 product containers per day. One mistake in this inspection process could cause serious harm or cause the entire lot to be recalled and disposed.

INVENTORY

The most valuable characteristic of bar codes in inventory control is keeping track of where the hundreds, even thousands, of parts which arrive at a company are stored or delivered. Like the bloodhound we described earlier, bar coding allows a company to find the right part precisely when it is needed. The information which is initiated by the wanding of a part number on a label is accurate and almost instantaneously available. The computer also automatically updates stock status and can immediately highlight and identify items which are running low. By wanding or keying in a part number, inventory personnel can tell how many of the

INVENTORY STOREROOM

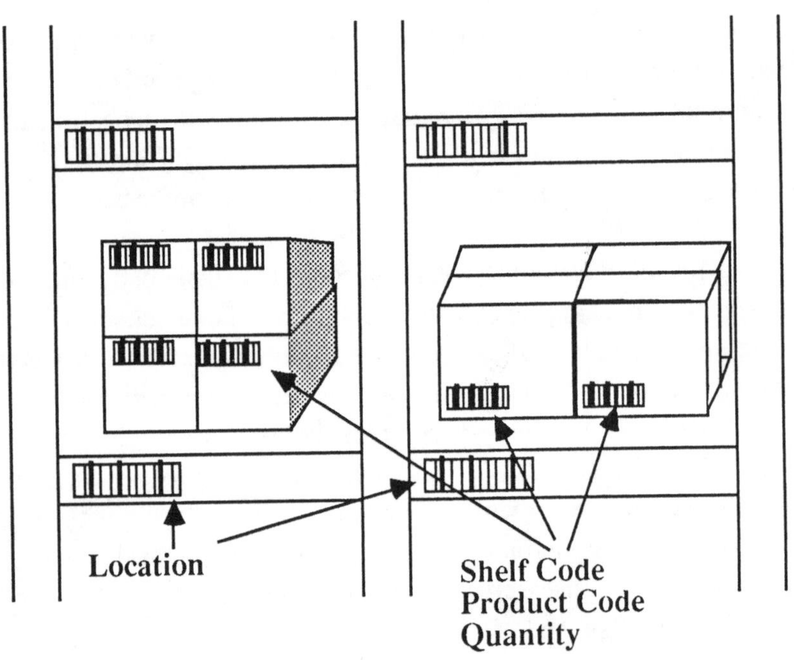

parts are available for any particular order and where those parts are located. This greatly increases the efficiency and productivity of a warehouse or storage area. Time is no longer wasted trying to locate parts and trying to reconcile inaccurate inventory counts with the actual physical inventory.

Keep in mind, however, that the goal of a JIT process is to eliminate or reduce inventory to its lowest level by using problem-solving techniques. We do not want to look at bar coding as a way of treating the symptom. We want to use bar coding as a tool to solve problems. Reducing inventory with bar coding should be addressed in a problem-solving manner, not as a stop-gap means to automate data collection.

For example, a warehouse employee has to kit ten parts for use in a particular assembly operation. She keys these part numbers into the system or wands the part numbers in from a menu. The computer then generates a pick list which not only tells her how many parts are available, but where each item is located in the warehouse. She then takes a portable reader with her into the warehouse. When she arrives at the right location she scans the label attached to the shelf to verify that she is selecting the right part. The reader then prompts her to pick the necessary quantity. If she scans the wrong bin or part, the portable reader gives her a message to try the scan again.

After picking the correct quantity and item and loading them into her bin or tray, she then uses a menu attached to the portable reader to record the transaction. Instantly, the computer updates the stock status of this part, reflecting the depletion of inventory she has just taken off the shelf and allocating it to the right department. She then continues with the same routine for the other nine parts with complete confidence that she will find what she wants. The system will record all of the transactions she does for each kit which was assigned for picking.

In the area of inventory management, bar codes thus help a company do the following:

- **Keep track of dollar value.**
- **Prepare tax reports.**
- **Maintain a high level of accuracy.**
- **Reorder material, especially in a JIT environment.**
- **Keep a record of sales performance.**
- **Keep a record of demand.**
- **Control material location.**
- **Increase warehouse productivity.**

An electronics manufacturing company set these objectives before automating its inventory control system:

- **Maximize use of labor for:**
  - **Production counting.**
  - **Sortation.**
  - **Daily physical inventory.**
- **Reduce errors.**
- **Optimize use of space.**
- **Create an audit trail for every part and every transaction.**

The electronics manufacturer began implementing a bar coding system by placing portable bar code readers with display screens on its fork lifts. Pick lists which showed the part number, the storage location by aisle and shelf, and the quantity needed were displayed on the screen. The fork lift operator then used a laser to scan each item as he loaded it on to the truck. Once the item was recorded, the screen would display the next item to be picked. After the entire list was picked, the operator would then proceed to a terminal and download all the information in order to update the inventory. At the same time, the main computer system would generate a new pick list for the fork lift operator.

The pick lists, of course, reflected the need for the parts on the production line and were balanced with the capacity of the work station to which the parts were delivered. In reality, this is a JIT, or "pull" environment. The use of bar codes greatly reduces the amount of transcription or other errors. With fewer errors, inventory managers are able to trust inventory levels. This means that there is no need for excess inventory just in case the counts are wrong. Less inventory obviously means less warehouse space and better utilization of a company's resources.

Another company, a small retailer, uses bar coding in a more traditional inventory application. This company used to count inventory by tearing off one half of a tag attached to the item. All the tag halves were then sorted manually by location area and inventory levels were determined. This system was slow, error-prone and costly. The old method was replaced by bar code labels. Warehouse employees were then able to scan the label at its location and let the computer record quantities and location. In fact, this company now has a tracking system in addition to its inventory system. Parts are able to be scanned throughout the company. If the owner needs to know where a particular item is, in the warehouse, on the retail floor or at the shipping dock, he need only key in the part number and see where each item is and how many are at each location.

With the use of bar codes in their facilities, companies have been able to achieve savings as follows:

- **Warehouse space decreased by over 50%.**
- **Labor costs reduced by over 70%.**
- **Inventory levels reduced by up to 50%.**
- **Scrap levels approaching zero.**
- **Record accuracy increased to 98%.**
- **Data accuracy improved by 75%.**
- **Improved lot traceability.**

WORK-IN-PROCESS

The number of parts needed to assemble a product can range from the dozens to the thousands, depending upon whether you are building lawnmowers or rockets. But whatever you are building and however many parts you require, the same need to track parts through work-in-process (WIP) is present for all companies. What is needed is a system which directs the right part to the right place at the right time. This means that the system needs to know what the parts are and how many there are so they can be easily sent to the proper work station. A bar coding inventory control system, in conjunction with JIT techniques, is capable of this. What needs to be added is a system of identifying and tracking parts from one work station to another. The system should also be able to pull components from the warehouse when needed at the next operation.

This is a complicated task since production schedules vary and most companies are not fully aware of how many products are in process or at what stage of completion they are in. A bar coding system makes this all possible. Operators at the work stations are now able to wand a part or a subassembly as it arrives at the designated point in the production process. This alerts the system that another production operation has been completed and a new one is to begin. New shipments of parts can then be sent to the work stations which need to be replenished.

Pro-Tech Director Phil D. Stang pointed out at a recent seminar for the University of Wisconsin that bar coding can even help in reducing the set-up times for equipment at a work station. Die and tooling location, movement and timing are vital to facilitating rapid and accurate change-over of production. The employment of bar coding accelerates the information flow between the database and the work station and thus allows the operator to "do it right the first time." There is no more wasted motion or time as the operator searches for the right tools. A portable bar code reader will tell him if he has wanded the correct tool.

In essence, a WIP bar coding application gives a company the opportunity to access "real-time" information, not what was planned or what happened yesterday, but what is going on right now on the production line. That knowledge is the first requirement in any decision-making activity. "Real-time" information also means a company does not have to operate with excessive levels of WIP inventory. If a company has an order for 10 products, then a "pull" system can be implemented to ship only the amount of parts needed to build ten assemblies. If the order changes to 12 or drops to nine, then there is no guessing about how much inventory to hold back or send ahead to the production line. The new amount will be pulled by the floor or operator. Bar coding always comes back to timely and accurate information. Isn't that what all companies need?

One manufacturing company has also used its WIP bar coding system to report rejected parts. As a tray of parts arrives at the work station, an operator scans the label on the tray and then scans each part. If a bad part is found, he then scans a reject control code on a menu. This timely update of information allows production managers to ship more parts to the work station in order to replace the defective ones. Of course, from our standpoint, this is not the best solution. Defective parts should never get inside the receiving room's door. If this company had a Supplier Certification program, then it would have been able to convince its supplier to use bar coding in order to obtain quality and production control at the source.

SHIPPING

Bar coding enables companies to automatically sort shipments by order and by carrier. In a typical shipping application, orders are called up on a display screen. Scanned items are then checked against bar code labels on shipping orders as the packages are loaded on to the truck. Trucks themselves can carry identifying labels so that a shipment is not put into the wrong carrier's truck. An incorrect order or an over- or under-shipment causes the display screen to sound an alert. Back orders can then be immediately identified.

SHIPPING

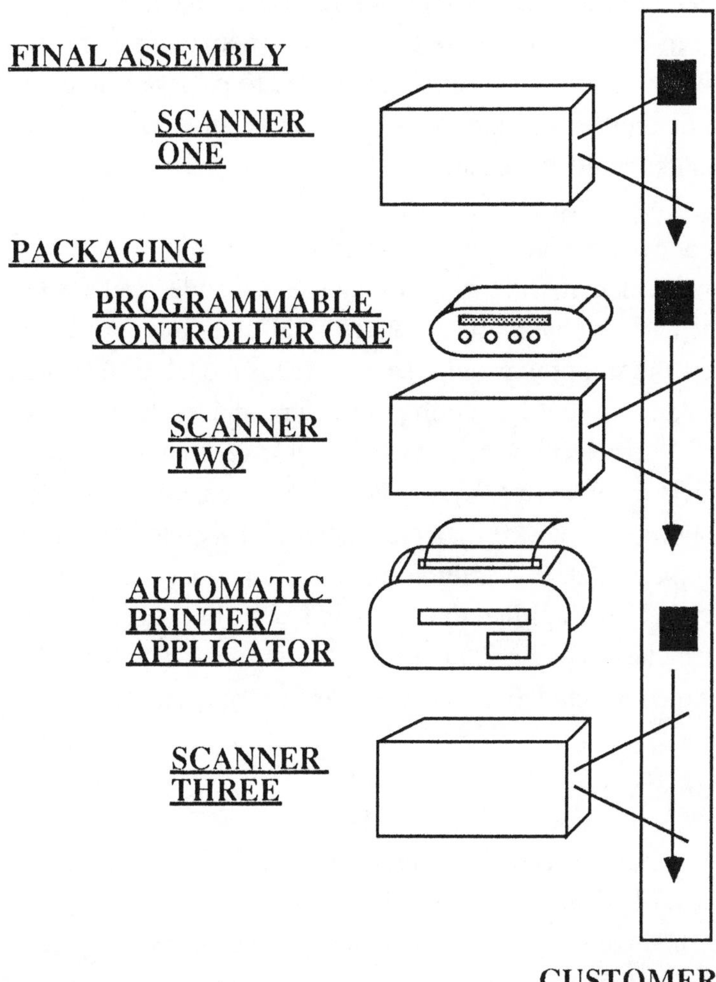

One small appliance manufacturer uses bar coding to weigh packages and then to assign shipping zones and rates. This has eliminated an error-prone and time-consuming manual system.

The bar codes on shipped items also allow the company to generate daily shipping reports as well as reports on shipping efficiency. In addition, the information collected during the shipping functions is then used to update the main computer system's database. This information is then used to print out invoices for each of their customers on a daily basis, thus improving their accounts receivable cash flow.

Bar codes also have a packaging application in the shipping area. At one truck manufacturing company, a bar code label is attached to each truck chassis as it leaves final assembly. As it moves toward the shipping room, a scanner reads the label and sends the information to the main computer. Here, the model is looked up in a table to determine how it will be packaged. The computer then instructs the conveyor system to route the chassis to the correct packaging area. Once it arrives there, it is scanned again before being packaged. A printer at the site then generates another bar code label to be applied to the outside of the package. Finally, the packed chassis arrives at the shipping area where a third scanner reads the label and directs the package to the right carrier's truck.

TOOL ROOM

With a manual tool tracking system, it is never entirely clear which tools are assigned to which employees, where the tools are, what the inventory levels are and even whether the tool has been returned. Because of this confusion, companies often stock two to three times the amount of tools which is actually needed. Certainly, some buffer is needed for broken or damaged tools, but much of the buffer today is the result of workers hoarding tools.

Most workers simply don't trust that a tool will be available when they need it to complete a job, so they, in effect, use the tool room to supply their own private tool rooms on the job.

Bar coding can eliminate most of these problems by providing a system which governs check-in and check-out of tools, keeps a record of where all tools are and who has them, insures that the right tool is assigned to a job and establishes a maintenance program for tooling. All this is accomplished by first wanding a bar code label on the employee's badge. This registers the user's name and department in the computer. Then the tool itself is wanded to link it to the user's name. Every tool, of course, has a unique bar code label. More sophisticated systems can even generate reports showing daily check-out levels for each tool or maintenance schedules. These reports can be used to adjust the number of stocked tools up or down as the demand requires.

Companies using bar coding in tool rooms have reported increased levels of confidence by workers. Hoarding is no longer a large problem because employees are now sure that the tool they require will be there.

ROUTINGS

Bar coding has two major applications for routing. It can sort parts on a conveyor system as they move past a scanner. The necessary routing information is contained in the computer system. By scanning the bar code label on the part, the reader triggers the computer to send instructions to the various gates on a conveyor system. By opening or closing gates, the computer shuttles the part to its correct destination.

Bar coding also aids in the routing of parts through the production process. Again, wanding the label as a part exits one work station will tell the operator or the conveyor system where the next stop in production process is. This allows the system to signal operators as to which parts are due at their work station. The part, the work station and the operator all have bar codes. As the part arrives at a station, the operator wands his badge and the label at the work station to indicate when and where he began working on the part. He then wands the part label to record its arrival and to verify that it has been routed to the correct work station.

Perhaps the most common example of routing is what is found at an airport terminal. A tag is placed on your baggage bearing a bar code symbol. This tag has been printed from information entered into the airline's computer either when you bought the ticket or when you checked in. Your tagged baggage then goes through a series of readers which direct the luggage to the gate where your airplane waits.

QUALITY MANAGEMENT

Bar coding allows companies to collect quality data on a real-time basis both in the field and at the plant. Inspectors or operators can process the data directly into the company's database. It is then a simple matter to request the computer to generate reports based on the following variables:

- **Yields.**
- **Feedback.**
- **Generic failures.**
- **Serial numbers.**
- **Work-In-Process.**
- **Final Inspection.**
- **Managing time in holding areas.**

This information can be printed into reports which production, purchasing and design teams can analyze to correct frequent problems. Records of rework and other production errors by work station, employee, lot number, supplier, etc. can easily be logged into the computer by scanning the part's bar code label and wanding a code on a menu for the type of problem.

The computer, aerospace, drug and health industries, which require high manufacturing standards and careful collection of quality data from procurement to final inspection, already use bar coding in data collection. One manufacturer of computer circuit boards has put scanners at each of its seven inspection points on the factory floor. There, operators scan the boards to make sure they have all been through the process in the correct manner and to record any failures. Since every board carries a bar code label which triggers the part's history in the computer system, any failure can be quickly traced back to its source. Instead of spending hours, even days, tracking down the cause of a faulty part, quality control personnel can now locate the problem almost instantaneously. This bar coding application also solves quality problems in which the wrong configuration of chips is placed on a board. Incorrect parts would cause the bar code reader to display an alert on the display screen. In such a situation, an operator could not proceed if he wanded the wrong chip. Bar coding also gives us visibility into how long something has been held for disposition. For example, if a product is wanded as a reject, the system reviews the age and advises the appropriate department and user group.

BAR CODING APPLICATIONS IN ADMINISTRATION

DOCUMENT TRACKING

Bar codes aid companies in monitoring paper flow simply by

creating a "card file" for all the documents in the main computer system. When you want to find a book at the library, for example, you don't search through all the shelves to locate the book. You go to the card file and look up the book. The card contains a unique number assigned from the Dewey Decimal System. Your task is then greatly simplified. The number directs you to the proper shelf and, since the shelves are arranged in numerical order, finding the book presents no problem.

Borrower Searching Card File with Scanner

The same principle is at work in bar coding company documents and paperwork. Whenever a form or report is created or received, a unique bar code label is put on the form and a record created for the computer by keying in the appropriate information. Every time a document is checked in or out (just like a library book) or processed in any way, the bar code is scanned and the additional information is keyed into the computer. Once the document is in some kind of storage area (a file drawer, for example), the computer keeps track of its location. If the document is removed, the "borrower" scans her own access label and the document label so that the computer has an updated knowledge of the document's location. As can be readily seen, this application of bar coding can also limit access to secured information. The computer can be programmed to allow or not to allow different operators the ability to "take out" a document.

Bar coding also simplifies the process of changing documents. One of the most prevalent uses of this application is in making revisions to engineering drawings. As changes are made, the computer keeps a record of every change, who made it and when they made it. Thus, there is not only a way to quickly move engineering drawings in and out of files through the tracking application, but a historical record as well. The savings in time and money due to fewer errors or even lost drawings results in higher productivity. Production now has the latest drawing, free of red marks, and can build the part without constant problems or requests to Engineering for explanations.

Jerry Claunch points out that these applications are also a critical building block of "World Class Manufacturing" which relies heavily on timely and accurate inspection and work order data.

Follow-up paperwork is normally the least disciplined task of the Maintenance department, he adds. Bar coding applications which enhance data gathering and historical record accuracy are invaluable in supporting trend analysis and standard procedure development functions, both of which are crucial to continuous maintenance management improvement.

Another documentation application is shop floor data collection. Although done in the production area, the information is used in making administrative decisions as we noted when discussing quality data collection. Reports generated from tracking production via bar codes can be used by production, design, purchasing, accounting, sales or marketing departments. In fact, such information ties a company together by making the same information available to all departments at the same time.

ORDER MONITORING

In most respects, the application of bar coding to order monitoring is the same as its application to document tracking. More specifically, bar coding assists in the entry of customer orders and in their fulfillment. Once a customer order is entered into the computer system, a bar code label can be printed which will be attached to the sales order, the work order, the product itself and to accompanying documentation. An employee can then wand the customer's order number to find out where the order is in the production process. After production is finished, the shipping department can then use the same bar code to determine where the finished product is warehoused.

The use of bar codes greatly reduces entry and transcribing errors.

The customer order number and its lot number are encoded on the label so that an operator doesn't have to keep writing down the same number as the order goes through its various stages of production. The same errors are eliminated when the order is received as well. Order takers can use a menu to input due dates, quantities, part numbers, billing information, credit history, shipping instructions, etc. And all of this information is just a scan away.

With the application of bar coding in the area of customer orders, you can expect the following benefits:

- **Improved on-time completion of orders.**
- **Improved customer service.**
- **Ability to answer inquiries promptly and accurately.**
- **Ability to track all shop orders.**
- **Highlighting of orders behind schedule.**
- **Accurate accumulation of actual job costs.**

FIXED ASSETS

The application of bar coding to fixed assets was one of this technology's first uses. By attaching a label to capital equipment, office furniture, shelving and other permanent objects, companies are able to keep an account of what they own, to note the age of assets and to conduct physical inventories. One manufacturer attaches a label which contains the department name as well. This allows the company to scan the assets for each department separately and then to generate reports for management's review.

TIME AND ATTENDANCE

Bar coding also greatly speeds the task of gathering and processing labor information. This is accomplished by assigning workers a laminated identification badge with a specific bar code. Instead of punching a time clock when they start or end work, they have their badge scanned by a card slot reader which automatically updates their payroll records. Such factors as lunch breaks, lateness penalties and job pay rates are also automatically updated by the software which drives the bar coding system. It is even possible to break down precisely how much time was spent at each task during the work day. The operator merely scans his badge as he begins and ends each job. The gathered information can then be used to generate labor reports and to assign job costs to the production of a job lot. It is common to reduce the amount of time spent checking in and out by as much as 80 percent.

JUST-IN-TIME APPLICATIONS

In the preceding applications, we have often referred to the ways in which bar coding enhances Just-In-Time (JIT). Let's take a more detailed look at this relationship and at bar coding's relationship to Total Quality Control (TQC) and Computer Integrated Manufacturing (CIM). In our experience, we have noted that JIT, TQC and CIM are closely related and are best defined and discussed as a business philosophy which we call the Total Business Concept (TBC). TBC is the result of the interaction between these three elements. It is committed to quality and efficiency in every operation or procedure which a company undertakes, as we have already seen above. TBC is actually the result of an evolutionary process which began with the introduction of Material Requirements Planning (MRP) and Manufacturing Resource Planning (MRP II). The next stage was the adoption of JIT/TQC as the governing management concept. The stage we are approaching is one in which we tie all the parts of a company together into a network — the TBC network which links the parts through the exchange of common and vital information. It's clear then why bar coding is so important to the application of the TBC philosophy. Bar coding, as we have repeatedly said, is really a technique to ensure the rapid, accurate and reliable exchange of information. The two were meant for each other.

TBC is the place where the flow of material and the flow of information merge together into one river which eliminates waste, reduces costs and guarantees high quality. And this river sweeps into many different areas of a company, some of which are listed here:

- **Raw material identification.**
- **Materials handling flow.**
- **Work-in-process.**
- **Prints and engineering.**
- **Job sequencing.**
- **Alternate routing.**
- **Robotics usage and routings.**
- **Rejected material and disposition.**
- **Rework status.**
- **Data retrieval.**
- **Inspection and quality control.**
- **In-process stocking.**
- **Finished goods movement.**
- **Shipment and traffic routing.**

For these areas to function in a TBC environment requires accurate, rapid and reliable collection of data to solve problems like the ones on the next page.

- **Inaccurate inventory reporting.**
- **Tracking of material in WIP.**
- **WIP queues.**
- **Inspection backlogs.**
- **Paperwork backlogs.**

As we have noted above, bar coding aids TBC by collecting data to resolve these problems. Bar coding helps track and direct the right material in the right quantity to the right place at the right time in a manner which fits with the TBC rule to eliminate waste. All data collection is the result of a one-step process — the action of scanning a bar code label.

No company can expect to merge bar coding with JIT/TQC or CIM, however, without convincing top management of its vital importance and long-term benefits. Bar coding and TBC must be part of a company's overall strategic plan. The next chapter addresses the benefits that can be expected from the implementation of bar coding and how to cost justify an implementation.

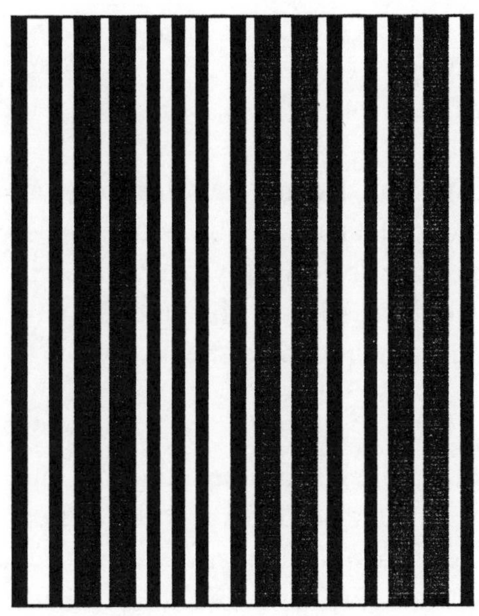

CHAPTER SEVEN: Cost Justification

No company can expect to implement bar coding without convincing top management of its vital importance and long-term benefits. The selling of a bar code system to top management begins with a summary of what bar coding can do for a company. This introduction also includes answers to the question of why a company should implement a bar coding system. The remainder of the presentation entails laying out the costs involved in getting the project started (and maintaining it) and describing the numerous savings and benefits which will result from the installation of a bar coding system. In other words, "How much is it going to cost?" and "How much is it going to save me?" To be successful, companies must measure and report actual performance versus planned performance.

WHAT BAR CODING CAN DO

By themselves, bar codes do nothing. It is the coordination of all the elements we have discussed so far that makes bar coding a wise investment. Bar coding helps create a balanced system which will increase the confidence of employees in the computer system. This will allow you to use your computer more effectively and to its full capacity.

Automated scanning does not require human operators, and thus eliminates transcription errors and the need to hire more clerical help. This does not mean the elimination of jobs. We always tell our clients to take the people whose job has been eliminated and retrain them to do other work in your company. Finding experienced people is difficult. There is no reason you should eliminate people who already work for you and have a good sense of how the company functions.

Bar coding provides information which was not previously available to both operators and supervisory or managerial employees. Better information translates into better control of the company. Better control means increased productivity so you consistently get the right material to the right place at the right time. How long do you have to wait for material now? And, when it arrives, how often is it the wrong material? Bar coding can help you answer these questions positively.

Bar coding does not require extensive user training. As noted before, operators can learn to use a scanner or light pen in less than 15 minutes. Of course, that does not mean a company invests just 15 minutes in training and education. Nor does it mean that only operators are taught about bar coding. As will be shown in the next chapter on implementation, we recommend that education and training be an on-going project and that it not be limited to users. All levels of personnel, including top management, must receive education or else they will not back the project simply because they do not understand all of bar coding's possibilities and benefits. Cost justification, then, can be thought of as the first step in the education plan.

Bar coding can help improve relations with your suppliers as well. More effective control over work-in-process inventory also increases control over material requirements and lead times. This will mean that you are able to order raw material with greater accuracy. Thus, suppliers will know what to ship you with greater precision. In other words, both you and your suppliers can enter into a partnership where Just-In-Time delivery and Total Quality Control is the norm, rather than the exception. Bar coding's accurate tracking of material needs provides for better production schedules.

Bar coding can track customer orders on the shop floor which will save time and aggravation and reduce the number of disputes with customers. How many times does a sales manager have to leave her desk to find out the status of an order? With bar coding, she calls up the information on the screen as she is talking on the phone. What does this say to the customer? This company knows what is going on. It has control over its operation. It doesn't put me off with excuses. I can trust them to deliver when they said they would. I'm going to order from this company more often.

Bar coding speeds up clerical functions. One company we have worked with had a three-week lead time producing one of their products. Five days of this lead time was spent in manually processing the order. With bar coding, they reduced processing time to 24 hours, thus gaining four manufacturing days.

Bar coding will let companies become more flexible. The goal in manufacturing is to have such an integrated system that a company can produce lot sizes of one. Smaller lot sizes, however, mean more transactions. But, in a bar coding environment, more transactions doesn't have to mean more mistakes. Bar coding can handle the increased paperwork and transfer of information rapidly and accurately. In fact, bar coding can eliminate the paperwork all together and place it all in the computer system where it would be available to whomever needed it.

Bar coding has a demonstrated payback period. A bar coding system will pay for itself in less than three years, often in less than one year and, not so rarely, in less than a quarter.

START-UP COSTS

Not all of the costs below are one-time outlays of cash. Education and training, for example, is necessarily on-going since new employees must be taught how to use the scanning equipment and how to use the system information. The following areas are typical:

- **Orientation**
- **Education and Training**
- **Designing a Label** — what type of paper, printer, reader, environmental concerns.
- **Packaging Changes** — standard packages, label fit.
- **Cost of Printer(s) —** how many and where
- **Cost of Verification Tool** — to see if label will read and if doesn't, why not.
- **Label Applicator Costs** — Automatic application machines vs. labels attached by hand.
- **Computer System Changes** — New or modified software and hardware.
- **Cost of Reader(s) —** how many and where
- **Training at Supplier** — acquainting suppliers with vital need for quality labels.
- **Learning Curve** — how long will it take for personnel to use the system effectively.
- **Facilitation Costs** — electrical, furniture, cubicles, rearrangement of racks, etc.
- **Concentrators —** depends upon number of stations

ON-GOING COSTS

These are costs you can expect to pay after a bar code system has been implemented:

- **Labels, Ribbons and Supplies**

- **Warranty and Service Costs**
- **Replacement of Equipment or Parts**
- **Labor Time** (putting on labels)
- **Potential Obsolescence Cost**
- **Communications Costs** — setting up new networks and communications lines.

HIDDEN COSTS

The following costs are sometimes overlooked or underestimated:

Commonality — This was once a major issue since companies would have to buy a different reader for every symbology. Now that reading devices can handle a number of different symbologies, however, one type of scanner can handle most of the bar code labels which are attached to products shipped by suppliers.

Store Assembly — Depending on the way in which products are arranged for shipping or storage, it is possible for companies to underestimate the number of labels they will need to bar code.

Error Recovery — Money must be spent for a back-up system in the unlikely event of a system failure.

Label Shelf Life — Either more money must be spent to purchase labels which last for a long time or to reprint and reapply labels on a maintenance schedule.

Label Problems — Problems such as glue bleeding or excessive adhesive strength often mean redesigning bar code labels.

Flexibility — If a company has the need to print many unique labels, there will be a need for an on-site printer in appropriate areas. Also, if the mainframe computer handles the printing chore, it is likely that there will be a need for a programmer.

Production Issues — With bar coding, there is often a need to change or develop new production procedures. For example, the application of bar coding to time cards requires an up-front cost to buy the equipment and train employees. This cost will be offset, however, by savings in paperwork and in checking time cards in the front office. With bar coding, these tasks are now automated. Each company will have to determine on its own whether the cost of bar coded time cards is justified.

Inferior Quality — Labels produced by inferior printing equipment are the most deadly cost of all. They can spell the difference between success and failure. This hidden cost is best avoided by spending money. It's far better in the long run to buy the highest quality equipment you can afford.

Service Response — There is the cost of additional inventory of wands, etc., if the equipment fails.

SAVINGS AND BENEFITS

What benefits can I expect from the application of bar coding? Almost too many to name. From the receiving to the shipping door, bar coding has a direct impact on labor productivity, production control, operation costs, customer services, space requirements and inventory control. Bar code systems are also relatively easy to implement. They do not require great outlays of money for operator training. And since they allow automatic entry and retrieval of information, they reduce transcription errors and free up operators to do productive work. No longer is it necessary for workers to spend inordinate amounts of time doing reporting tasks.

The following partial list of bar code benefits shows the areas in which an implementation will improve your Return on Investment (ROI):

Production — reduced lead time increases production, reduces inventory and increases business by showing responsiveness.

Reduced lead time
Improved tracking
Smaller lot sizes
Reduced material handling
Employment of JIT
Utilization of purpose robots
Enhanced flow management
Higher capacity utilization
Higher manufacturing flexibility

Quality — better quality means less scrap and a better view of production problems.

Total Quality Control

Labor — reduced time leads to more output; reduced overtime means less labor added when business increases.

Less repetitive clerical function
Eliminated functions
Reduced labor requirements
Increased labor efficiency

Inventory — savings is the cost of carrying inventory.

Reduced inventory investment
Improved inventory accuracy
Increased inventory turn rates

Control — accuracy improves system reliability; increased responsiveness translates into increased sales; less borrowed money increases savings.

Complete functional integrated system
Improved total accuracy
Elimination of batch processing
Increased management control
Improved cash flow — electronic billing
Reduced postage — electronic billing

Customer Orders — more sales and less cost of goods.

Increased accuracy of customer shipments
Increased order fill
Reduced truck demurrage
Reduced lapsed-order delivery time
Improved customer-inquiry response time
Improved customer-inquiry quality

COST MANAGEMENT

How much does it cost to collect and enter data? If manual, how much for salaries? What is the cost of inaccuracy? What is the value of having the reputation of being a producer of quality products which are delivered on time? How much does excess inventory cost? What is the value of timely and accurate information? Many of these questions relate to the principles we have covered at length in our earlier books. All of the questions, however, actually are variants of one central question:

HOW DO I REDUCE WASTE?

Cost justification, then, is built on the premise of reducing waste, of becoming more efficient and accurate, just the qualities that bar coding possesses.

Cost management has served all types of organizations. It has survived because of its ability to capture, record, measure and communicate the cost of operating a business. Cost management has evolved through the years as the business environment has changed. This evolution has led the way for new ideas and concepts to help us measure and predict our operations and to cost justify new methods and implementations.

We define cost management as a two-part process:

1. **The management of cost whether or not the cost has direct impact on inventory or the financial statement.**

2. **Management's commitment to the continual reduction of the elements of cost whether or not those costs can be measured in purely financial terms.**

TOTAL COST

In keeping with this definition of cost management, the definition of cost has changed as well. Cost is now defined as total cost, or ***all cost attributable to the sale, manufacturing and distribution of products***, as shown in the following diagram:

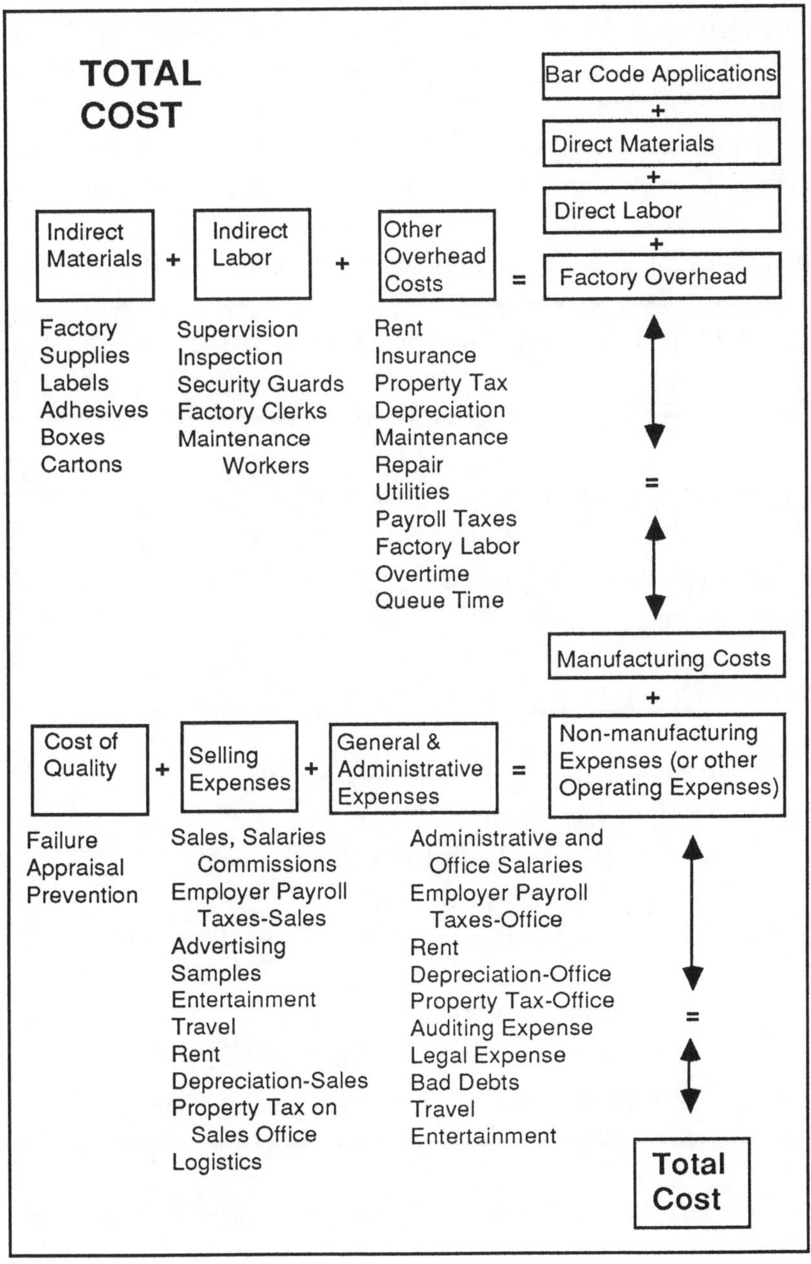
TOTAL
COST
Bar Code Applications
+
Direct Materials
+
Direct Labor
+
Indirect Materials
+
Indirect Labor
+
Other Overhead Costs
=
Factory Overhead
Factory
Supplies
Labels
Adhesives
Boxes
Cartons
Supervision
Inspection
Security Guards
Factory Clerks
Maintenance Workers
Rent
Insurance
Property Tax
Depreciation
Maintenance
Repair
Utilities
Payroll Taxes
Factory Labor
Overtime
Queue Time
=
Manufacturing Costs
+
Cost of Quality
+
Selling Expenses
+
General & Administrative Expenses
=
Non-manufacturing Expenses (or other Operating Expenses)
Failure
Appraisal
Prevention
Sales, Salaries Commissions
Employer Payroll Taxes-Sales
Advertising
Samples
Entertainment
Travel
Rent
Depreciation-Sales
Property Tax on Sales Office
Logistics
Administrative and Office Salaries
Employer Payroll Taxes-Office
Rent
Depreciation-Office
Property Tax-Office
Auditing Expense
Legal Expense
Bad Debts
Travel
Entertainment
=
Total Cost

This definition moves companies away from a dependence on price analysis as the major criterion for determining costs. This is because cost analysis examines all costs involved in the process of manufacturing products, whereas price analysis uses the seller's price without examining or evaluating the separate elements of cost and profit which make up the price. Cost justification relies on a total cost approach based on this formula:

TOTAL COST = VARIABLE COSTS + FIXED COSTS + SEMIVARIABLE COSTS

COST IMPROVEMENT

Financial control becomes a much simpler task as we focus on cost improvement:

<u>9-STEP COST IMPROVEMENT METHOD</u>

1. Identify Targets and Opportunities
2. Describe Them in Detail
3. Identify and Define Possible Problems
4. Set Objectives and Goals
5. Gather Facts and other Related Information and Analyze the Data
6. Determine Solutions
7. Evaluate Solutions and Alternatives
8. Implement Techniques to Solve Problems
9. Evaluate and Measure Results

The cost justification begins by identifying cost targets. Second, the team will describe the targets. The aim here is to note all costs, apparent and hidden, which are associated with the target. Third, define the problems you are experiencing within these areas so that, fourth, you can set objectives. As with other areas of JIT, the rule of halves applies here as well. That is, you should seek to reach your goal by reaching a point half way between where you start and where you want to be. Once achieved, the new point becomes half the remaining distance to the goal.

Fifth, gather facts which will enable you to suggest possible solutions and analyze the data. Coming up with these hypotheses is the sixth step. Seventh, evaluate your solutions. This is where the team becomes vitally important. Any solution you choose will have effects throughout the company. Have people on hand who can tell you how it will affect the operations and procedures in their individual departments. Of course, some areas are more greatly affected than others. Therefore, it is not necessary to have the whole company sit down and debate the merits and demerits of a proposed solution. Each company will find an optimum size for the team and a most effective make-up.

Eighth, implement the solution which the team has determined to be the most effective at cutting costs. Needless to say, the implementation, itself, must be cost-effective as well. Ninth and last, evaluate the results of your implementation and either try another solution if results aren't as planned or move on to the next target point, if you have been successful.

Cost improvements can be either short-term or long-term. The chart on the following page shows some typical cost targets.

The cost improvement framework will help you identify a number of targets requiring your attention. Although we find that many

Targets	Number of Transactions	Cost per Transaction	Savings
Absenteeism			
Turnover			
Accidents			
Distribution			
Warehousing			
Mail			
Maintenance			
Materials			
Supplies			
Meetings			
Paperwork			
Purchasing			
Quality			
Telephones			
Time management			

companies (whether large or small, whether food processors or manufacturers of office furniture) have similar problems, we also realize that the dynamics of your particular situation will have a great impact on your solutions. That is why it so important to use a team to understand the dynamics of cost improvement.

COST JUSTIFICATION

How do you cost justify? By demonstrating that the implementation of bar coding will improve the following areas:

- **Customer Service**
- **Throughput**
- **Process Yield**
- **Labor Efficiency**

And reduce:

- **Inventory**
- **Product Recalls**
- **Fixed Assets**
- **Labor**

The first step in cost justifying a bar coding system is to build a cooperative mind-set with all departments and levels of the company. Through education and training in the Just-In-Time/ Total Quality Control philosophy, they will learn how to identify cost drivers or opportunities for reducing costs. The following analysis of opportunities is typical for a bar coding implementation:

ABC COMPANY

	Man-months	**Capital**
Close the loops		
Prepare detailed design	1.0	-
Develop and implement basic feedback control	2.0	-
Purchase and install controllers	-	$20K
Purchase and install sensors	-	$20K
Evaluate and refine control logic	1.0	-
Develop and implement process model	2.5	-
Develop and implement balance of plant	2.0 - 6.0	-
Improve reporting		
Evaluate existing reports	1.0	-
Modify reporting software	1.0 - 3.0	-
Totals	10.5 - 16.5	$40K

These are the objectives at this stage:

- Collect total cost information.
- Measure performance.
- Isolate and identify issues.
- Highlight cost reduction opportunities.
- Eliminate levels of controls.
- Do a cause and effect analysis.
- Utilize problem-solving techniques.
- Eliminate waste.

Start cost justification by listing 15 to 20 categories. Estimate how much you can reduce each category. Don't come up with reductions by yourself as the project leader. Go to the areas in your company and ask: If you had the proper inventory, tools and facilities, how much could you reduce that number? You will find out that a 2% reduction here and a 5% reduction there soon add up to a considerable saving of money. Bar coding can typically reduce costs by 5-20% in each category. Furthermore, by diffusing the cost reductions over a number of areas, you increase your chances of hitting the final number. If, for example, you are seeking to save $1,000,000 and one category falls short, there is an equally strong probability that another category exceeded your estimate.

The following are examples of some of the categories that we recommend using in a cost justification of a bar code system:

FREIGHT

With improved inventory accuracy, there should be less of a need for rush orders from suppliers which have to be shipped air freight. How much money could you save here? A conservative estimate would be 10%.

OVERTIME

If, like many companies, you find yourself shipping a majority of your orders during the last week of the month, then overtime accounts for a large part of your labor costs. But, with improved tracking of orders through work-in-process and improved inventory accuracy, there is no excuse for this end of the month crunch.

PRODUCT QUALITY

How can we control the process so that it can't make bad products? Less scrap means more productivity for the same amount of dollars.

QUALITY OF LIFE

Go to the personnel department and ask them what the level of employee turnover is in your company. How much money do they spend on advertising new positions? How much do they spend on orienting, educating and training new employees? Then ask them what would happen to these numbers if the jobs were less stressful. If the company had a bar coding system which increased control and made it less necessary to fight fires, how much would they estimate that these costs would drop?

REDUCED INVENTORY

Does material arrive at work stations as it is needed? How much inventory is in work-in-process? What is the cost of carrying inventory? Bar coding can significantly reduce inventory levels by getting the right part to the right place at the right time.

INCREASED SALES

If bar coding now allows you to build quality products on time, by what percentage could you increase sales?

Other categories, such as customer service, freight, warranty premiums, repairs, use of temporary employees, physical inventories and work-in-process, would be asked similar questions. A 10% savings in 15 to 20 categories soon adds up to a large number. The point is to make all of these reductions "do-able," that is, don't force numbers on people which are impossible to meet. The users must identify and commit to the improvements, not the leader of the project. Many small bites add up to a large reduction as can be seen in the chart below:

ABC COMPANY	PLANT ONE		PLANT TWO	
	Cost	Benefit	Cost	Benefit
Types of Equipment	$60K	$200K	$30K	$100K
Labels	$20K	$125K	$10K	$70K
Design	$25K	$100K	-	$75K
Software	$30K	-	-	-
Hardware	$20K	-	$20K	-
Totals	$155K	$425K	$60K	$245K

Note that a second plant does have the same start-up costs as the first plant. However, the savings can still be accomplished from plant to plant by using what we developed for Plant One. A successful reduction in costs, even if it is moderate, increases morale tremendously. This strategy of selecting an area with visible paybacks is part of the overall implementation strategy.

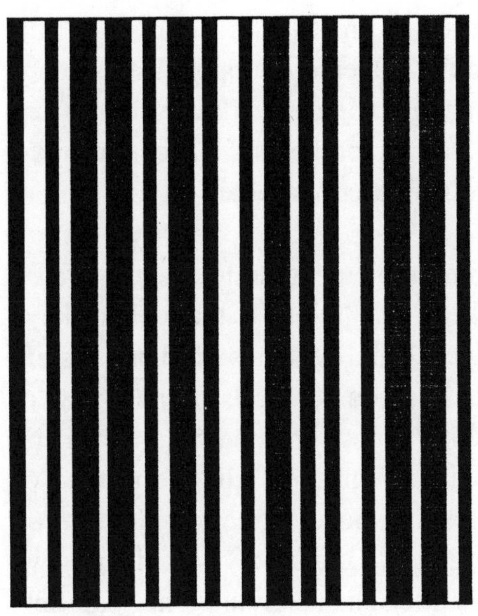

CHAPTER EIGHT: Implementing a Bar Code System

The most successful way to implement a bar coding system is to gain top management commitment. There are several ways in which we can gain management support. One way is to forward articles, books, reports and pieces of information such as seminars being held on the topic that include the tangible benefits of bar coding to the top levels of our companies. Another way is to arrange for on-site visits to plants which have embraced bar coding so management can see a total business concept in action. Procuring outside consulting assistance from a person with knowledge of bar coding applications and implementation will also shorten the learning curve and provide quicker results. Still another method of gaining top management support is to select a small part of your company and implement a pilot project before tackling the whole company. A plan for the total business project, however, is still needed if you choose this route.

In fact, there are three different implementation strategies which we call "cold turkey," "parallel," and "pilot." In the "cold turkey" approach, a company just dives in and switches from one system to another. If the old system ends on June 30, the new system begins operation on July 1. This is not a method we recommend unless your company is small enough to handle the myriad of details or is not in danger of losing valuable time and information when problems invariably come up. Cold turkey is something we recommend for dinner the day after Thanksgiving. The "parallel" approach attempts to run the old and new program simultaneously until the new system has reached a point where it can handle all the work. The degree of difficulty in this approach is directly related to how much difference there is between the old and new systems. The greater the difference, the more difficult this approach is. And whenever the new and old approach do not match, there is a tendency to rely on the old approach because people know how to work the old system no matter how bad it was.

The "pilot" approach is the least stressful and most successful approach being utilized today. By selecting a small area, perhaps one aisle of a storeroom, a company has the opportunity to test the equipment and label design in a real-life situation. Whatever problems crop up can then be addressed immediately. With this phased implementation, a company is also able to use the experience gained from the pilot area to train the people in subsequent implementation areas. We recommend choosing a pilot area with the most visible paybacks. It could be an area which is most in need of improvement and/or it could be one in which you are assured of success.

There is one final way to get management commitment. A story which we addressed in our Supplier Certification book illustrates the point:

> Two business people, one Japanese and one American, are at an international manufacturing conference held in Africa. One afternoon, they decide to explore a nearby national game park. They are happily snapping away when they notice some lions approaching.
>
> They run back to the car but it is stuck in the mud.The American starts shaking in his boots, but the Japanese sits down and starts putting on some sneakers.
>
> The American looks at him as though he's crazy and says, "You can't outrun those lions!"
>
> "I don't have to," replies the Japanese. "I just have to stay one step ahead of you, the competition."

Keeping Ahead of the Competition

Competition is an excellent impetus to get top management commitment to a bar coding system. It is an undeniable fact that a company looks to its leaders for direction. Middle management is always ready to embrace a program if upper management is committed. People at lower levels in the company are ready to accept change, provided they are given the responsibility and authority to act and that there is direction from above. But, we need to overcome accepted practices which have conditioned top management to make all the decisions. A bar coding program requires internal departments, customers and suppliers to work as a TEAM.

TOTAL BUSINESS CONCEPT (TBC) STRATEGY FOR IMPLEMENTATION

The key to the creation of a framework for continuous improvement is teamwork. The implementation and achievement of bar coding consists of four activities:

1. **Top Management Commitment** — establish ground rules, goals, objectives and a sense of direction.

2. **Team Administration** — administer the formation and implementation of the action plans.

3. **Training and Education** — educate and train all levels of your company, direct labor, supervisors, managers and customers in bar coding.

4. **Performance Measurements** — initiate program reviews and provide ongoing support at various levels of the implementation.

Only minimal expenditures are needed to improve communication, to involve the workforce in problem-solving and decision-making as it relates to bar coding, or to develop interdepartmental cooperation. And since direct labor will work with management on teams, there is an opportunity for both to develop techniques on how to work together. With this level of cooperation, learning curves are quickly diminished, thus lowering the total cost of the implementation.

In effect, the creation of a company culture fosters the vision, responsibility, authority and accountability which Just-In-Time demands. We can think of the above activities as four pillars which support a roof. Take away one pillar and the structure crashes to the ground.

Thus, a bar coding program is really no more than a program to collect data for management decision-making. To get there means applying the Total Business Concept approach, a journey from exposure through orientation and education to program review and on-going support.

The left side of the chart shows the planning phase. It consists of three steps:

> **Bar Code Education** — communicate a consistent message about the program throughout the company.
>
> **Assessment and Opportunity Review** — identify where bar coding opportunities exist and what benefits will ensue.
>
> **Action Plan** — develop a one-year plan which defines the costs, directions, objectives and goals for success.

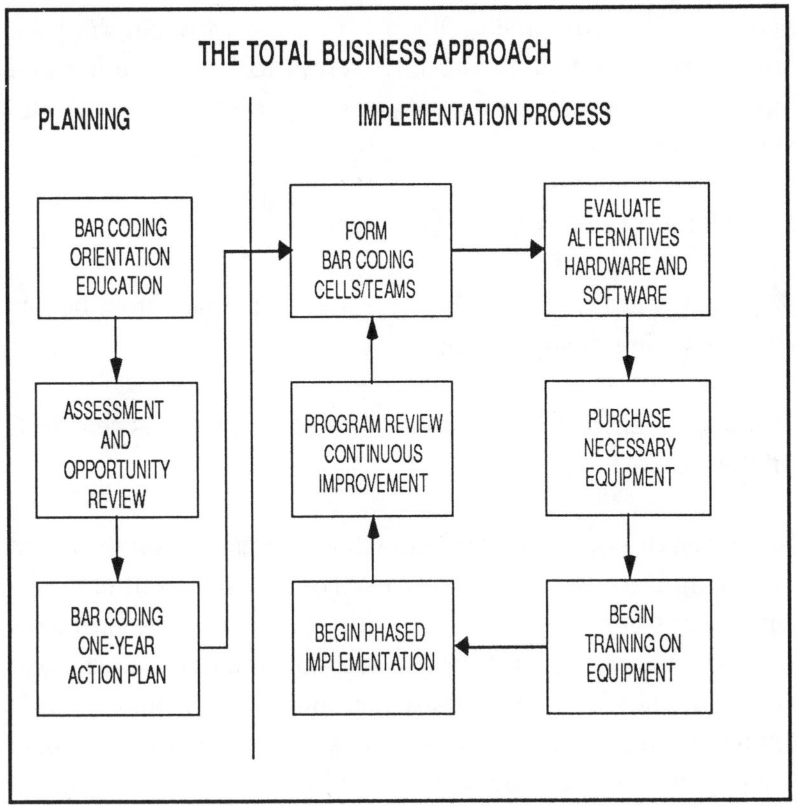

Management's involvement in this phase is to provide guidance, vision and direction to the implementation teams.

The right side of the chart is the implementation phase which consists of six steps. In step one, we form teams that are required to address issues identified in the assessment and opportunity review process. The next step is to evaluate alternative data collection system, hardware and software. In the third step, the company negotiates, selects and purchases the necessary bar coding equipment. Next, the individual teams are given proper training on the equipment. The fifth step is to begin the pilot phased implementation. The last step is to keep refining and improving the process so that there is always continuous improvement.

BAR CODING PLAN OF ACTION

Progress toward the goal of a successful implementation begins with answering this question:

How are we gathering information now and what is required for the future?

Only when this question is raised will a company be on its way to addressing the real business issues. Top management commitment means building an environment where creative problem-solving is the norm. This can be accomplished as we establish goals and objectives and exercise risk analysis with our people. It will require the development of trust with your people, suppliers of equipment and components as well as with your customers. Delegation of responsibility and authority to the lowest levels of the organization must be accomplished.

The next step is to form a planning team which evaluates the present business system in terms of gathering, processing and reporting data. Its job is to determine what the company needs and wants, whether a bar coding system can be implemented to satisfy a customer's requirements or whether it will be expanded to include internal operations as well.

Before a company can start this task, however, it must understand what a team is and how to form it.

WHAT IS A TEAM?

> ***A team is a group dedicated to a common goal, who rely on each other's strengths and fill in for each other's weaknesses.***

The results of a team will be greater than the sum of efforts made by individuals. Even though a company is made up of autonomous parts, they add up to a whole. Teams are made up of individuals from a number of disciplines within a company and from its suppliers. We recommend that a minimum of 50 percent of the team be direct labor and a maximum of 50 percent be from the ranks of management. This assures participation by the operators and users of the system. Remember, however, that a team must have the authority and responsibility to make change happen.

The group itself should be an interdepartmental team consisting of eight to ten people from the vice president level to direct labor. We must be sure to include people from the areas of Material Management, Purchasing, Information Systems, Production, Process Engineering, Product Engineering and Finance. In some cases, it may be a good idea to invite customers and suppliers to serve on teams in order to be sure requirements are met.

The steering or project team involves itself in the preparatory and planning phase of the bar coding journey:

1. **Exposure to Bar Coding through orientation, training and education.**

2. **Assistance in the preparation of an opportunity and readiness assessment.**

3. **Development and creation of a company vision and first year action plan.**

4. **Development of an education and training plan based on the model below.**

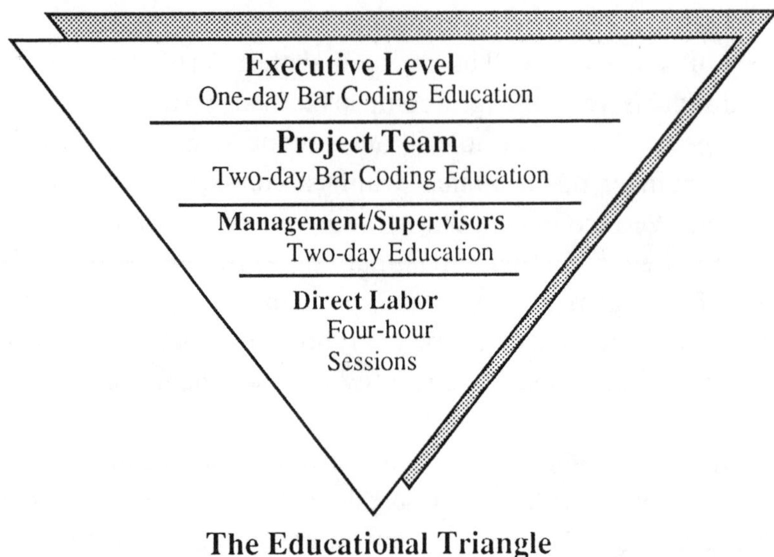

The Educational Triangle

The project team defines how bar coding can provide benefits to the company, reviews projects, provides resources and guides the overall effort of continuous improvement. The team has the responsibility to create the culture change and maintain that environment.

PLAN OF ACTION STAGES

STAGE 1: ASSESSMENT AND OPPORTUNITY REVIEW

This stage consists of preparing the assessment and opportunity and should incorporate an evaluation of the present information gathering system and determine future goals and objectives. The activities to be covered are the following:

- Determine company goals.
- Review company operations.
- Analyze management of information system.
- Identify scope of process.
- Define informational needs and goals.
- Identify where bar coding can be applied.
- Design the bar code labels and what appears on them.
- Select a printing method.
- Develop a system design.
- Define human resource issues.

System Design

There are several system designs from which the bar coding team can choose. A company can tie its bar coding system directly to the existing mainframe computer. It can connect to a distributed minicomputer which serves other functions as well as bar coding. Bar coding can be connected to a dedicated minicomputer which is used only by the bar coding system. Or, individual bar code terminals can be linked to one of the above choices through a port concentrator which acts as a gateway. The diagram on the next page shows what these configurations would look like.

Whatever your choice, there are many questions which need to be answered. Systems design is an important component of the implementation. Time must be taken to formulate realistic objectives from the information which will be collected. Then, upon

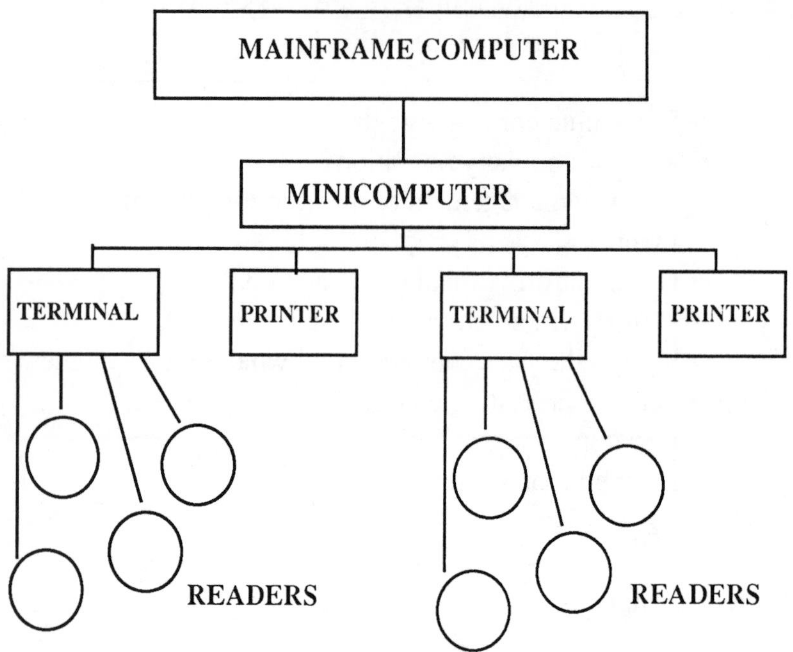

A Bar Code System Design

that foundation of information, you can begin to build a system which meets your needs, instead of having a system which forces the organization to meet its needs.

The checklist which follows will provide you with an idea of the type of information for which you will be searching. No checklist, however, can be complete without knowing the circumstances and environment at a particular company. Please bear in mind, then, that our checklist is a guideline, or a prompter, which will help you begin your own system design.

SYSTEM DESIGN CHECKLIST

Overall Design

____ Describe your objectives and the scope of the system in writing.

____ Ask the question "Why?" five times.

____ Write a functional specification that describes how the system will work.

____ Organize the flow of information so those involved with the project will get what they need to know, when they need it.

Automatic Identification Technology

In terms of price, performance, proximity, portability, ease of training and environment, which technology is best for the company?

____ Magnetic strip
____ Radio frequency
____ Optical character recognition
____ Vision
____ Magnetic ink character recognition
____ Bar coding

Bar Code Technology

____ Amount of information to be encoded in the symbol (number of characters).

____ Data content: Alphanumeric or numeric

____ Available space for symbol. Symbol dimensions.

____ Check digit needed?

____ Off-site or on-site printing?

____ Exposure of label to environmental conditions—weather, dirt, oil, etc.

____ Quantity of labels to be printed per day.

____ Method of applying bar code labels.

____ Method for verifying bar code reliability.

STAGE 2: PROPOSAL

In this stage, the project team prepares a report which defines recommendations and benefits. It should include what information the company needs to capture and why it is needed as well as the correct equipment and actual budget required.

STAGE 3: DEVELOPMENT

After the proposal has been approved, the team identifies system specifications, software and hardware requirements, and quality control or verification needs. The following list presents ome of the implementation costs which will need to be addressed:

- Programming—custom or readily available.
- Installation—internal/external assistance.
- Training and education requirements.
- Testing, pilot and phased approach to implementation.
- Evaluation of alternatives and successes.

STAGE 4: IMPLEMENTATION

Once the funds are allocated for the purchase of hardware and software, the team's representative from Purchasing negotiates the contract. Besides installing the system, the team will also need to integrate the new bar coding system with the present data processing system. One issue to address is who should train people in the use of bar coding equipment. Lead times for bar coding equipment range up to four months. The implementation stage can be up to six months when you add the up-front work required.

STAGE 5: EVALUATION

While the bar coding system is being implemented, the members begin the next stage in which the system is monitored. The team should be assessing whether the system is working as planned and whether goals are being met.

USERS — THE KEY COMPONENT

Throughout the implementation of bar coding, one must remember that, on its own, bar coding can result in contributing to the profit of the company. Bar coding is a tool which will assist in increasing productivity, reducing inventory, eliminating waste and improving profits. It is how people use bar coding that makes the difference.

Itzhak Perlman can play Mozart on the violin. The music he produces carries us away with its beauty. If one of us were to pick up that same violin, all we could do is produce squeaks which would make an onion cry. It's the same tool; the user makes the difference. A different violin wouldn't help us. Only the education and experience of a Perlman would produce a great performance.

Bar coding is no different. A company can spend tens to hundreds of thousands of dollars and install the greatest system in the world and the result would still make onions cry until it has educated its people in the use of the system.

We have been witness to several situations in which divisions within a company buy the same bar coding system. Some divisions play Mozart; many make onions cry. But we want to hear American success stories.

Bar coding does not produce profit. People who know how to use the system do. Bar coding systems cannot be installed like a piece of office furniture which will sit against a wall and cut costs. When a system is selected, there should be defined paybacks other than anticipated financial advantages such as increased data accuracy, reduced inventory investments and improved delivery service. Success should be predicated on how well the people who use it in their day-to-day tasks are doing.

As discussed, a key element in bar coding implementation is identifying available opportunities for each department. A rule of thumb is that if it is counted, accounted for, or moves, there is an opportunity for bar coding. For example, in the receiving and accounts payable departments, parts are counted to ensure that accounting only pays for what is received and accepted. What about material time management? Was the material delivered on time from the supplier to the receiving dock, from the receiving dock to work-in-process (WIP), and from WIP to the customer?

Success is improving on what has been done in the past; each business activity involving the customer through the receiving department must be defined as to its role in the business. In most implementations, this is one of the more difficult steps to accomplish. People don't want to make commitments for which they will be measured. However, studies indicate that these same people want recognition for a job well done. The effort required is selling it to the people. A company can't improve unless there is a plan and measurements in place to direct and monitor its activities. This task becomes much easier to accomplish if upper management has already been educated about the principle of measurement and control.

PERFORMANCE MEASUREMENTS

Today, we must use yardsticks which will provide us with information to make decisions. Data allows companies to compare actual data against predicted performance. This provides an opportunity to take corrective action. This is the definition of proactive:

***To measure
the predictability
of the outcomes
of decision-making
in real time.***

Defining the role of each business activity and developing performance measurements is relatively simple. Measurement must get back to grass roots. Management must use the system to improve accuracy and the timely management of basic data and activities. On the next page are some measurement suggestions:

Function	Measurement	Why
Accounts Receivable	Aging of Receivable	Ensure timely receipt of dollars
Accounts Payable	Aging of Payable	Displays dollars commi-tment
Design Engineering	Accuracy of Bills	System integration affects many other users — Accounting, Planning, etc.
	Timely Completion of Engineering changes	Ensure prompt updating of BOM structure files
Materials	Level of Investment	Monitor and control in order to reduce inventory
	Degree of Accuracy (on-hand and on-order)	Same as Accuracy of Bills
	Active vs. Inactive Inventories	To act on the inactive
	Location control	To monitor spare utilizations
Purchasing	On-Time Delivery	To support production needs, but also provide ability to measure suppliers
	Actual Lead Time vs. Planned	System integration; impact on inventory investment
	Supplier Reject/Quality Performance	Monitor to initiate corrective action and accumulate data for statistical performance
Production	On-Time Delivery	Same as Purchasing

Actual Lead Time	Same as Purchasing
Past Due Aging	To minimize schedule misses
Aging of Open Orders	To ensure control over work order in manufacturing and minimize unknown variances for old orders. To close orders in a timely manner
Quality Performance	To measure rework, scrap and in-process flows

The objective of measurement in a bar coding system is to track the progress of the implementation. Many companies, once they have received the funds for implementation, fail to track the payback. Our approach is to provide the company with a system that pays for itself. Without establishing various tracking systems, we will be unable to witness our success.

CONCLUSION

The finest bar coding solutions are available to us. But the real gains in American productivity will result from giving people better tools, educating people on how to use them, and measuring results to achieve maximum utilization of the system.

The complex problems which we will face in the future cry out for more improvements and higher profits. Bar coding is a step toward the goal of internal and external control. But bar coding is only as good as the imagination, commitment and creativity of the company implementing a system. Our intent, then, has been to show you what ***you*** can do with bar coding. Good luck on your journey!

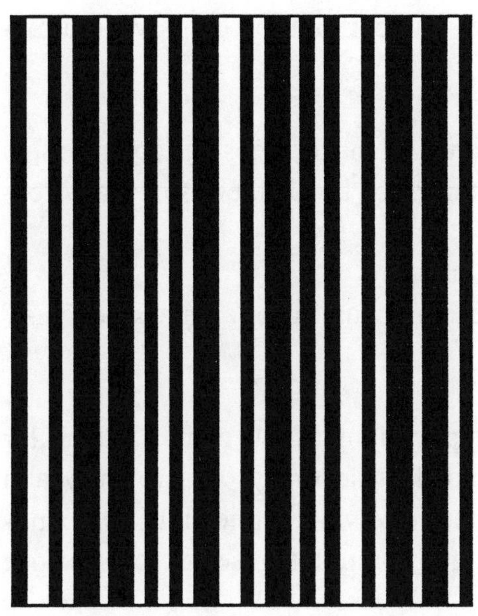

CHAPTER NINE: Bar Code Case Studies

The following case studies are all derived from actual work done at clients of Professionals for Technology Associates, Inc. (PRO-TECH), an international management counseling and education firm, and from discussions with people knowledgeable in the area of bar coding applications.

Prime Computer
Manchester, New Hampshire

Prime Computer is a developer of CAD/CAM/CAE hardware and software. The corporation has sales of approximately $560 million. The Manchester plant, which has been in operation for seven years, employs 250 people. The corporation employs approximately 4,500.

Walter Merrill, Plant Materials Manager, sees bar coding as an extremely important communication link in the business environment.

"It is the ultimate link between humans, materials and machines," he says.

Merrill also believes the applications of bar coding extend far beyond increased speed and data accuracy of data entry and material tracking. He lists the following applications as obtainable by all companies willing to commit themselves to the effort:

ELECTRONICS INDUSTRY APPLICATIONS OF BAR CODE

- Supplier Participation (Bar Code Material Shipments)
- Material Tracking (Receiving, Stockrooms Work-In-Process)
- Quality Defects Analysis
- Capital Assets Identification
- Shipping Documentation
- Physical Inventories/Cycle Counts
- Distribution Centers

- Field Service
- Employee Badge Identification
- Pal/Prom Control
- Q/C Inspections

"As for purchasing," Merrill continues, "the most critical area is supplier participation. We begin by educating our suppliers about bar coding objectives. Then we supply them with labels at first and show them how and where to apply them.

"We move gradually until all suppliers comply. I think this is the key to our success. We don't impose our system on them. We work with our suppliers in a partnership."

The results are truly impressive. Prime Computer's facility is a clean, organized and pleasant workplace. The complete material flow is tracked via bar code from the receiving dock to the shipping dock. Information is fed into the facility's on-line materials system as material flows through inspection, testing, stockroom, kitting and work-in-process. Bar code labels are applied to parts or boxes of parts so that they will either be stored or sent to the appropriate point on the production line. Labels also identify where each product is in the assembly process. For example, it is possible to know that Thursday's shipment of sheet metal is now in the paint shop because the label contains receiving information.

What information a label contains is, of course, subject to some limitations, but how it is used is only subject to your imagination. Bar coding supports MRP and MRP II which, in turn, forms a base for JIT. Prime Computer utilizes the ASK MAN/MAN manufacturing resource planning system on a fully integrated basis. Such coordinated information is vital to the attainment of the ultimate JIT goal — the right material in the right place at the right time.

Gunther International, Ltd.
Mystic, Connecticut

Gunther International, Ltd., is a designer and manufacturer of modular products for use in the processing of high-volume, computer-generated documents. Their total system approach allows customers to combine modules to perform a number of functions. At the heart of the system is a laser reader capable of reading and processing bar coded sheets of paper at speeds between 20,000 and 36,000 pages per hour.

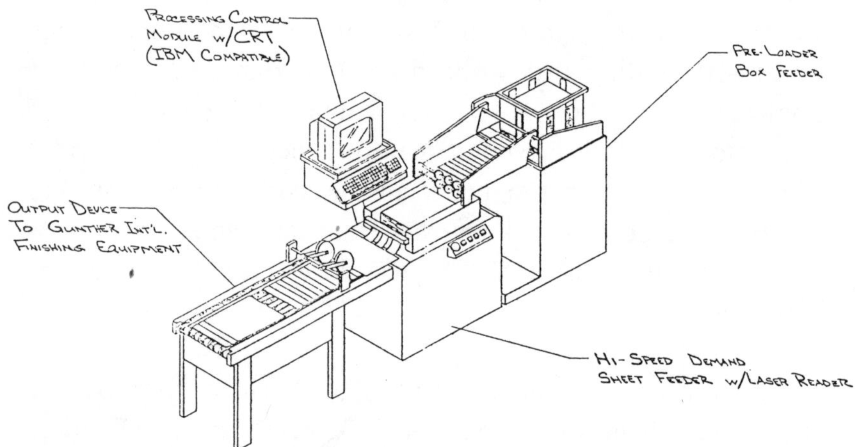

Gunther International F300

Ned Beaver, National Sales Manager, says that at these speeds "the integrity of the contents of a package or envelope must be guaranteed." Gunther's equipment maintains this required level of integrity by using a laser reader which is capable of scanning a bar code up to 600 times per second. The software which drives the system will not allow a document to continue until there are three consecutive good reads. Mr. Beaver also points out that the software maintains an audit trail of every bar coded document.

Each bar coded sheet, for example, is composed of an account number, page number, total pages in group and function instructions. These function instructions tell the system what to do with each sheet of paper. Some of the encoded functions instruct the different modules to take the following actions on the appropriate sheets:

- Feeding
- Binding
- Banding
- Enveloping
- Manifesting
- Stapling
- Folding
- Inserting
- Metering

The bar coded sheets enable the system to maintain control throughout the processing functions listed above. Bar codes also verify that the package of printed material is complete and in the proper sequence. They guarantee processing security and integrity, provide a complete audit trail and proof of mailing and determine variable postage automatically.

These controls are critical, Mr. Beaver explains, in the insurance, finance, health care and publishing industries which are among the principal users of the equipment. He reports that the company's insurance clients stand to save "hundreds of millions of dollars" with the use of bar coded paper processing. He notes, for example, that in the insurance industry each state has its own regulatory agency. This means that every policy requires certain additions or omissions unique to that state. Furthermore, these requirements frequently change as state legislatures enact new laws. Because of this situation, the amount of preprinted policies which became obsolete in the warehouses of insurance companies ranges between 30 and 40 percent. The error rate in manual picking at one company, Mr. Beaver reports, was as high as 80 percent.

With bar coded pages and inserts, the insurance companies are now able to get the right documents into the right package at the right time for the right client. Sounds like Just-In-Time? Mr. Beaver agrees and points out that the integration of his company's machinery to printing equipment virtually allows "Just-In-Time publishing."

Mr. Beaver also points out that the price of a mistake in an insurance policy or financial documents can be highly detrimental. The security and integrity of these documents is assured by bar codes.

How does all processing work in a real application? Mr. Beaver demonstrated how with an insurance package consisting of five different stocks of paper which is sent out to agents. In the first step, the letter and instructions to the agent come out of the high-speed laser printer. The bar code (which is often placed on the binding edge of the paper) is read which instructs another module of the system to staple the letter and instructions. In step two, the agent's copy of the declaration comes off the printer. It, too, is stapled and put into the queue of package documents which is forming.

In steps three and four, the bar code on the instructions letter has also instructed another module of the system to drop a return envelope from one feeder and a statement, remittance and ID cards from another feeder into the queue. In step five, all of the documents and inserts are grouped in the proper order and are bound with a front and back cover. In step six, the whole package is inserted into an envelope to which postage is attached.

As noted before, any omissions, duplicates or incorrect sheets are immediately noted and the entire package is diverted from the run to be processed independently. So these mistakes are not repeated, the system has recorded all the steps of the process. Supervisors are then able to locate where the mistake occurred and what needs to be corrected.

This is just one application of bar coding. When asked about the future of bar coding applications, Mr. Beaver indicated that there will certainly be more innovations. But he also noted that the applications of the present technology are far from exhausted.

LAWRENCE AND MEMORIAL HOSPITAL

New London, Connecticut

Sylvia Poole, supervisor of the blood bank at L&M Hospital explained that the principal use of bar coding in her department is to help simplify the inventory management of blood products received from the Connecticut Red Cross Distribution Center.

Blood products received from the Distribution Center may include Packed Cells, Whole Blood, Fresh Frozen Plasma, Platelets, Cryoprecipitate, etc. Manual entering of these components into the computer system requires a longer time and allows for potential typographical errors.

Although this may not be the thousands of items of inventory stored at a large company, the need to keep an accurate product inventory count is absolutely critical. In very real terms, accuracy is a life-and-death issue. Ms. Poole also points out that the volume of shipments which come in during the week necessitates a system which allows blood bank personnel to process (and introduce) incoming products into the computer system quickly and accurately.

Ms. Poole explains that all blood products which are received from the Red Cross have attached bar code labels which use the industry standard, Codabar. The bar code identifies what the blood product is, what the unique unit number is, where it came from and medical information such as blood type, Rh factor, etc. One person is now able to receive the products, inventory them and log the information into the computer system.

The entry of a blood product into the system begins when a blood bank technician logs on the computer system. Ms. Poole demonstrated this operation at a computer terminal. She then selected a code for the entry of blood products. Next, she used a hand-held wand connected to a wedge reader to scan a bar code to read the Red Cross Distribution Center's code which indicates where the blood products came from. She then scans the label on the blood product which registers the component and container type into the system. The product's ABO/Rh is then entered. The expiration date of the product is entered manually when prompted by the computer.

There are several identical bar codes on the back of each red cell product. Ms. Poole says that one is attached to an index card. This is done so that blood bank personnel can use the inventory card to process products, instead of taking the products out of their refrigerated storage area.

As pointed out, the system also notes medical factors. One safeguard built into the system is continual "recaps" of all the processing steps which have occurred. For instance, just before the received blood product is accepted into inventory, a screen appears on the terminal which lists the following areas:

Entry (who entered the transaction)
Status (available or unprocessed)
Component (plasma, red blood cells, whole blood, etc.)
Container (single)
Volume (of container)
ABO (blood type)
RH (Rh factor)
Supplier ID # (unique number assigned to unit)
Receipt date
Receipt time
Expiration date/time of product
Any additional comments or special typings

Once a requisition is made by another department for a blood product, the wand reader is used to select the required product or products.

To issue the red cell product, a technician manually enters the date and time, then wands in the unit number, the supplier ID and the component type. A complete history is generated showing the allocation of the unit to a compatible patient or patients. For example, this is what a typical screen looks like at this point in the transaction:

ISSUE UNITS TO PATIENTS

DATE: 8/8/89
TIME: 11:40
Hosp/Acc/Unit No.: 33AA1111

Unit No.: 33AA1111 Component: Packed Cells Container: Single PC Volume: 350 ml Exp. Date: 9/9/89 ABO/Rh: A Neg

1. 112233 Doe, John W34
Doe, John (ICU)
Phys: 15 Smith, Jane

2. 556677 Johnson, Jack H55
Johnson, Jack (E-3)
Phys: 22 Black, John

Select No.: __

The blood bank technician can then select which patient is receiving the product. The technician issuing the unit will visually inspect the unit and will enter the IV nurse's name into the computer as the person removing the product from the blood bank. At all times, the blood bank knows the location of each unit of blood.

When one realizes, as Ms. Poole pointed out, that records of all blood product transactions are kept for five years, then it is no surprise how pleased she is with bar coding's ability to access this information quickly and accurately. Bar coding has made inventory management of blood products faster and safer.

MITCHELL'S SUPERMARKET
Niantic, Connecticut

Although founded in 1917, Mitchell's Supermarket, an $8 million a year independent grocer, did not hesitate to be the first grocery store in its area to implement a bar coding system. Joanne Mitchell, the store manager, reminded us that the system was first implemented in 1979. Note that this is many years before bar coding became a buzzword. What is even more remarkable is that the project was undertaken without the resources of a national chain.

Ms. Mitchell, however, pointed out that there were good reasons for their foray into the world of bar coding. And, even though one of the deciding factors in favor of implementation never materialized, Mitchell's found that many of their other reasons yielded results beyond what they expected.

"The major impetus behind the decision to go with bar coding was to save labor," she explained. "The idea was to use bar code labels on all our merchandise so that we would not have to stamp each item with its price. But this never came into play because a state law was passed which made it mandatory to put the price on an item as well as the bar code label. So we didn't save any labor there."

There were other reasons to implement the system, however, according to Ms. Mitchell.

"We wanted our cashiers to be faster and more accurate at the checkout counter," she explained. "When cashiers had to punch in the prices on a cash register, the average number of items per minute was between 14 and 18. With scanning, it's now 20 to 30 items per minute. And it's the customer who is most happy with this increase."

Anybody who has waited in line at a grocery store would certainly agree. Cashiers take care of customers almost twice as fast and rarely need to stop as they once did when an item was not priced. Ms. Mitchell, who first worked at the store as a cashier, remembers how she and employees would try to remember the price of items so that they wouldn't have to make customers wait. She freely admits that many of the prices that were guessed were not accurate. With bar coding, she pointed out, there is no need to guess.

"There is also no need to guess whether or not an item is taxable or what department it should be rung up on," she added. "All that is encoded on the label. Therefore, we get more accurate information on how each department is doing."

Keeping track of sales or promotional items was yet another reason for implementing bar coding at Mitchell's. Ms. Mitchell pointed out that this information can be used in various ways. One is to record the quantity sold in order to determine the store's margin. From this figure, Mitchell's can determine when to advertise and how much to spend. By using figures recorded from past years, Ms. Mitchell said that the store can also base their ordering of a sales item on the quantities of previous years. The sale of hot dogs during the Fourth of July is one good example.

Ms. Mitchell also said that the store recently used information captured by the system to reset the soda section of the store. This was accomplished by setting the sales figures for the various kinds of soda and then collecting information for three months. Based on these figures, Mitchell's knew which brands and flavors were fast movers and which were not and, thus, could allocate shelf space accordingly.

Although Mitchell's doesn't use their bar coding system for order generation or inventory counts just yet, Ms. Mitchell did say that the store is considering using bar coding in their receiving area. This would be done in coordination with their suppliers and wholesaler. Not surprisingly, Mitchell's wholesaler at the time was involved with the store's first implementation of a bar coding system.

Current training, Ms. Mitchell pointed out, is handled chiefly by a cashier who acts as a trainer. New cashiers are taught how to scan different types of containers and what to do if an item does not scan. They are also taught how to use the cash register if the system goes down in the event of a power failure.

Ms. Mitchell said that the biggest obstacle in setting up the system had little to do with the equipment. The Mitchell family quickly found out that the system needs time and people to support it. For instance, it took them some time to set up the files in the system. This was further complicated in the beginning by the fact that the system was not PC-driven. Reports and other information came out on the cash register tape. Now, Mitchell's has an NCR system which is controlled by a personal computer. Mitchell's has hired a part-time employee who maintains price changes and can use menu-driven routines to set parameters as needed.

Mitchell's current system is approximately three years old, but there is a substantial difference compared to the original implementation. For example, the store performs price checks in which every item in the store is scanned. In the "old days," each and every item was brought up to the cash register and scanned. Now, employees go out in the aisles and use hand-held scanners. The difference in accuracy is large. The store originally estimated that they were 88-90% accurate in the early days. Currently, they are running at 97-98% accuracy.

Mitchell's is not content to rest on its laurels. Ms. Mitchell indicated that they were already looking at new approaches. This system would allow the store to scan coupons which customers had clipped from magazines or newspapers or had received in the mail. Cashiers would scan the coupon at the checkout counter. The system would tell whether the coupon was valid, whether the purchased item was the correct one, whether certain manufacturer or store rules were met, and then automatically deduct the savings. For example: Has the customer bought some established dollar amount of groceries? This feature could also be used for coupons generated by the store.

The new system would also make the information on the customer's receipt more descriptive. This will increase customer service and satisfaction. Customers will be able to compare prices and increase accuracy.

When asked what Mitchell's would have done differently if they were given a chance to implement a bar coding system again, Ms. Mitchell replied, "We would have bought the new system we're looking at now, ten years ago." It was obvious from that comment that Mitchell's is committed to excellence.

JI CASE
Racine, Wisconsin

JI Case's Racine Tractor Plant manufactures large, two-wheel drive agricultural tractors ranging from 130 to 195 horsepower. The plant consists of 1.2 million square feet and employs about 750 people.

Steve Anderson, Manager—Industrial Engineering, says that bar coding was implemented on the tractor assembly line to collect Process Manufacturing System (PMS) information. The PMS computer system is used to view the current quality level of the plant's products by collecting defect and repair information. Bar coding is also used to enter the product's serial number and certification into the computer system for documentation purposes.

"The principal objectives of our bar coding system," says Anderson, "was to:

1. Reduce the time required to input data.
2. Improve the quality of input data."

Anderson explains that the PMS system, along with other shop floor controls, runs on a Stratus computer system. Operators at the plant use a light pen/badge reader interface at various terminal locations. Assemblers on the tractor line input information from a booklet of possible defects and repairs based on historical information. This is, in essence, a menu as described earlier in this book. The assembler uses a light pen to read the bar code next to the listed defect or repair. This information, which is stored in the system, allows personnel in the company to call up any particular serial number and read what operations have been performed. Thus, Tom Lueder, Director of Quality, points out, JI Case obtains a current view of the product's quality level.

The bar coding system was implemented with the launch of a new product line. It required an upgrade to the PMS system and took several months as the new product came on line. Anderson notes that there were no special problems beyond the normal bugs which had to be worked out of the PMS upgrade.

Before the implementation of bar coding, Anderson says that data was entered into the PMS system through the use of magnetic strip readers. There were problems, however, with this method. Magnetic strips became unreliable after wear had taken place.

Bar coding eliminated these wear problems. Bar code labels stand up to the wear and tear of shop floor work far better than magnetic strips. Consequently, the accuracy of data input with the bar coding system is very reliable. Now the plant can gather information which they know will accurately reflect the product's quality history. Such information is used extensively as a base for the plant's continuous process improvement.

Jim Barbieri, JIT project leader, points out that improvement is not limited to the manufacturing process. Although there was an improvement in the entering of data by bar coding over keyboard entry, time could still be saved. Internal computer operations require the system to search for the correct program code when the bar code is presented to the system. The search time to find the correct code for input is still the longest delay for data input.

JI Case's use of bar coding is a good example of how this technology can be used to input and organize information about processes as well as products. The use of menus which encode quality information in unique labels allows the company to go beyond more traditional uses of bar coding.

GENERAL FOODS
Dover, Delaware

While at General Foods, Pro-Tech Senior Vice President Jerry Claunch consulted with a team which was designing a bar code label (see below) to be placed on pallets holding 50-pound bags of cocoa. As mentioned earlier in this book, label design is a critical stage in the implementation of bar coding. Designing a label makes a team consider what information must be captured, how it will be read and under what conditions and how the information will be used. It is not merely the placement of a code's bars and spaces somewhere on the product. In addition to the above, teams must also consider whether the printer is capable of printing the necessary information and whether the readers can scan the information. In short, every factor in the implementation of bar coding has a direct effect on the label design.

The following memo was submitted to the plant. After a project review had been done, the memo reflected the present status of the labeling project and what issues had been dealt with.

MEMORANDUM

1. The attached label has been developed and is proposed as the model to be used for standardization.

2. The system currently being used is flexible and can be adapted to the project at a cost of approximately $5,000 for both software and hardware.

3. The new system is designed for the printing and reading of lower volumes of material.

4. High volume could be achieved with different hardware once funding is provided.

5. This label is compatible with PROS (operating system) and with the MRP II system presently being used at the facility.

6. To be decided: whether the label is pressure sensitive and whether the label should be applied directly to the shrinkwrap, on the pallet itself, or under the shrinkwrap.

7. Inbound labeling is not currently planned, but this label will support information and warehouse visibility.

8. This system has the capability to bar code all the lines of information presently on the label. Obviously, room must be made on some lines. This can be accomplished by abbreviating words or shrinking the type size.

As can be seen, this memo not only articulates present considerations but notes future considerations. Label design was executed with both the present and future in mind. The memo itself concludes with recommendations that the results be coordinated with suppliers and with other General Foods facilities and that a trial run be conducted with the bags of cocoa. The next step for this bar coding project is to present the design to management and leadership at the corporate or division level.

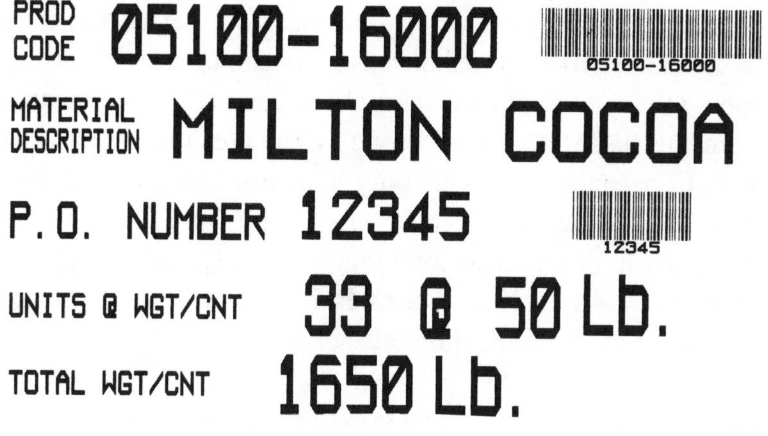

Package Label

COCA-COLA USA
Atlanta, Georgia

The principal reason that Coca-Cola USA has begun to implement bar coding is to reach higher levels of control and tracking of inventory, according to Senior Engineer Orlando Arjona.

"We're in the food products business," explains Mr. Arjona, "so it is critical for us to know where our products go, what their lot number is and where they are stored. Currently, Coca-Cola uses a computer system to keep track of inventory. However, much of the information is collected and keyed into the system by manual means. Mr. Arjona sees bar coding as making it possible for Coca-Cola to reduce labor costs since data entry with bar codes is done far more quickly than manual entry.

Equally important is the fact that bar coding reduces the errors in the tracking of inventory. Mr. Arjona points out that this translates into better customer service because "we can be sure that we are shipping the right product to the right customer." Error reduction also means less waste since wrong orders aren't returned to the plants. Consequently, productivity increases because time is no longer spent processing returns and trying to find why they happened. Mr. Arjona also notes that many of Coca-Cola's plants conduct daily physical inventories. Bar coding will greatly reduce or eliminate the time spent on this activity.

Steve Buffington of Coca-Cola says that the company also has an eye to the future with their implementation of bar coding. He notes that one customer who has a warehouse with bar coding tied to their inventory system has requested bar code identification on shipments from Coca-Cola received at their plant.

"We expect more customers to make the same request," says Mr. Arjona. "Bar coding is the wave of the future. In the 1990s, bar coding as an identification and data gathering tool will be widespread. We want to be prepared for that."

GLOSSARY OF TERMS AND ACRONYMS

AIAG—Automotive Industry Action Group

AIM—Automatic Identification Manufacturers

ALPHANUMERIC—Description of a symbology's character set which consists of letters and numerals.

ANSI—American National Standards Institute

APERTURE—Measure of the size of the beam which reads the bar code.

AUTODISCRIMINATE—Ability for one bar code reader to interpret several different codes.

CAD—Computer Aided Design

CAM—Computer Aided Manufacturing

CCBBA—Committee for Commonality in Blood Banking Automation

CCD—Charge Coupled Device

CHECK CHARACTER—Character added to guard against undetected errors.

CODABAR—Standard bar code symbology used principally by the blood products industry.

CODE 39—Standard bar code symbology and one of the most widely used.

CONTINUOUS—Symbologies in which intercharacter gaps are treated as characters.

CIM—Computer Integrated Manufacturing

DECODER—Converts signal from scanner into a signal which the computer can understand.

DENSITY—The number of characters which can be encoded in a given unit of length.

DEPTH OF FIELD—The distance between the closest and farthest point at which a bar code can be scanned.

DISCRETE— Symbologies in which intercharacter gaps are not treated as characters.

DOT MATRIX PRINTER—Printer which forms characters when an array of pins hits an inked ribbon which transfers the image to the media.

DRUM or **FORMED-CHARACTER PRINTERS**—Images formed from hammer striking ribbon and media against reversed image on a rotating drum.

EAN—European Article Number

ELECTROSTATIC PRINTER—Sensitized drum attracts toner which is transferred to media.

FIRST READ RATE—The ratio of the number of successful reads to the number of attempted first reads.

FIXED LENGTH—Description of a symbology which only allows bar codes of a set number of characters.

HEIGHT—Vertical measurement of a bar code.

HIBCC—Health Industry Bar Code Council

INK JET PRINTERS—Controlled jets of ink spray from nozzles to form image.

JAN—Japanese Article Number

JIT—Just-In-Time

LASER ETCHERS—Burn image into media or burn protective coating off of media to form image.

LED—Light Emitting Diode

LOGMARS—Logistics Application of Automated Marking and Reading Symbols

MAGNETIC STRIPE—Technology allowing the encoding of information on special labels with magnetism.

MRP—Material Requirements Planning

MRP II—Manufacturing Resource Planning

NUMERIC—Description of a symbology's character set which consists of only numerals.

OCR—Optical Character Reader

OPTICAL THROW—Least distance at which a scanner can read a bar code.

PRINT CONTRAST—Ratio of the difference of reflected light between the bars and spaces of a bar code. Print Contrast equals Space Reflectance minus Bar Reflectance divided by Space Reflectance.

QUIET ZONE—Area leading or trailing a bar code with no encoded information.

READER—A bar code scanner and decoder.

REFLECTIVITY—Amount of light reflected back by the surface upon which the bar code is printed.

RESOLUTION—Measure of the size of the spot of light reflected back to the reader.

SCANNER—Bar code device which produces a signal representing the bars and spaces of a bar code.

SELF-CHECKING—Ability of a symbology to guard against undetected errors.

SOFTWARE SHELL—Simulates keyboard entry of bar code signals.

START AND STOP CHARACTERS—Character which tells a scanner or reader when a bar code begins and ends.

SUBSTITUTION ERROR RATE—The ratio of the number of incorrect characters to the total number of entered characters.

TBC—Total Business Concept

THERMAL DIRECT PRINTER—Forms images by pressing heated areas of printing head against heat-sensitive paper.

THERMAL TRANSFER PRINTER—Forms images by pressing heated areas of printing head against heat-sensitive ribbon which presses against media.

TQC—Total Quality Control

UCC—Uniform Code Council

UPC—Universal Product Code; standard symbology used by the grocery and retail industries.

USS—Uniform Symbology Specifications

VARIABLE LENGTH—Description of a symbology which allows bar codes of varying numbers of characters.

VISION SYSTEM—Vision systems digitize an object's image so that it can be understood by a computer.

WEDGE READER—Converts bar code signal into a keyboard signal which the computer is able to read.

WIDE-TO-NARROW RATIO—Ratio of the wide bars to the narrow bars in a symbology.

WIDTH—Measurement of the narrowest element of a bar code. Same as **"X" dimension.**

"X" DIMENSION—Measurement of the narrowest element of a bar code. Same as **width.**

BIBLIOGRAPHY

Peter L. Grieco, Jr., Michael W. Gozzo; **MADE IN AMERICA: The Total Business Concept**, PT Publications, Inc., Plantsville, CT.

Peter L. Grieco, Jr., Michael W. Gozzo, Jerry W. Claunch; **JUST-IN-TIME PURCHASING: In Pursuit of Excellence**, PT Publications, Inc., Plantsville, CT.

Peter L. Grieco, Jr., Michael W. Gozzo, Jerry W. Claunch; **SUPPLIER CERTIFICATION: Achieving Excellence**, PT Publications, Inc., Plantsville, CT.

ACTIONLINE, Kathleen Vokes, Managing Editor; Automotive Industry Action Group, Southfield, MI.

BAR CODE NEWS, Russ Adams, Editor; Laura Hanson, Publisher; North American Technology Inc., Petersborough, NH.

AUTOMATIC I.D. NEWS, Mark David, Managing Editor; Douglas C. Edgell, Publisher; Harcourt, Brace, Jovanovich Publications, Cleveland, OH.

ID SYSTEMS, Carl T. Helmers, Jr., President, Editorial Director; Helmers Publishing, Inc., Peterborough, NH.

SENSORS, Dorothy Rosa, Managing Editorl; Christopher S. Crocker, Publisher; Helmers Publishing, Inc., Peterborough, NH.

H. Thomas Johnson, Robert S. Kaplan; **RELEVANCE LOST: The Rise and Fall of Management Accounting**, Harvard Business School Press, Boston, MA.

Armand V. Feigenbaum; **TOTAL QUALITY CONTROL**, McGraw-Hill Book Co., New York, NY.

PRODUCTION AND INVENTORY MANAGEMENT REVIEW and APICS NEWS, Raymond G. Feldman, Editor; Richard D'Alessandro, Publisher; Hollywood, FL.

PURCHASING MAGAZINE, James P. Morgan, Editor; John F. O'Connor, Publisher; Cahners Publishing Co., Newton, MA.

W. Edwards Deming; **QUALITY, PRODUCTIVITY AND COMPETITIVE POSTION, MIT Center for Advanced Engineering Study**, Cambridge, MA.

HARVARD BUSINESS REVIEW, Theodore Levitt, Editor; James A. McGowan, Publisher; Boston, MA.

Thomas J. Peters, Robert H. Waterman; **IN SEARCH OF EXCELLENCE**, Warner Books, Inc., New York, NY.

Philip B. Crosby; **QUALITY IS FREE**, New American Library, New York, NY.

FORTUNE, Marshall Loeb, Editor; James B. Hayes, Publisher; New York, NY.

MODERN MATERIALS HANDLING, Ray Kulwiec, Editor; William G. Sbordon, Publisher; Cahners Publishing Co., Newton, MA.

MATERIAL HANDLING ENGINEERING, Bernie Knill, Editor; George Horrigan, Publisher; Penton Publishing, Cleveland, OH.

MANUFACTURING SYSTEMS, Wayne L. Rhodes, Jr., Executive Editor; Arnold E. Keller, Group Publisher; Hitchcock Publishing Co., Wheaton, IL.

Long, C.J. (Chip); **IMPLEMENTING A BAR CODING SYSTEM**, Automatic ID News, Cleveland, OH.

INDEX